MAGNETIC ALLOYS AND FERRITES

MAGNETIC ALLOYS

AND

FERRITES

Consulting Editor
M. G. SAY, Ph.D., M.Sc., M.I.E.E.

Contributors
F. BRAILSFORD, Ph.D., B.Sc. (Eng.), M.I.E.E.
F. KNIGHT, A.M.I.E.E.
W. S. MELVILLE, B.Sc. (Eng.), M.I.E.E.
B. W. ST. LEGER MONTAGUE, B.Sc.
M. G. SAY, Ph.D., M.Sc., M.I.E.E.
C. GORDON SMITH, M.A., M.I.E.E.

WITH 115 *ILLUSTRATIONS*

LONDON
GEORGE NEWNES LIMITED
TOWER HOUSE, SOUTHAMPTON STREET
STRAND, W.C.2

First published . 1954

QC757
55269
c

PRINTED IN GREAT BRITAIN BY THE WHITEFRIARS PRESS LTD
LONDON AND TONBRIDGE

PREFACE

THE past few years have seen remarkable developments in magnetic materials, which have, in turn, contributed to progress in electrical equipment design. Quite recently, for example, among the magnetically-soft materials, grain-oriented silicon-iron alloys, ferrites, and grain-and-domain-oriented nickel-iron alloys have passed from the research stage to established production. Iron and iron-alloy micropowders and a range of ferrites have similarly been added to the already considerable list of permanent-magnet materials.

The wide variety of materials now at the disposal of the electrical engineer and component designer demands an extensive knowledge. Properties and limitations must be understood if skilful use is to be made of a unique and extending range of remarkable technological devices. The object of this book is to provide that information.

A revealing account of modern views on the fundamental processes of magnetization—including the domain theory—is given by Professor Brailsford in the first section of the book. The related subjects of materials for magnetic recording and magneto-striction, together with magnetic compensating and non-magnetic alloying are included.

M. G. S.

CONTENTS

1. FERROMAGNETIC THEORY

By

Professor F. Brailsford, Ph.D., B.Sc.(Eng.), M.I.E.E., Mem.A.I.E.E.

GENERAL

From the magnetic point of view all natural substances may be classified as diamagnetic, paramagnetic or ferromagnetic. The magnetic permeability of the materials in the first two groups, however, differs so little from that of free space that, to the technologist, they are " non-magnetic " ; but quite different are the ferromagnetic elements, nickel, cobalt and iron, which display magnetism to an extraordinary degree. With these elements as constituents a wide range of ferromagnetic alloys of practical importance also may be made, though there are some, the Heusler alloys, which include only non-ferromagnetic components.

The Magnetization Curve

If we have a long, uniform specimen in a long solenoid having a magnetomotive force of i ampere-turns per metre, then, using the rationalized m.k.s. system of units, the magnetic field strength $H = i$ amperes per metre (A/m). The flux density in the sample is $B = \mu H = \mu_r \mu_o H$ webers per square metre (Wb/m²), where $\mu_o = 4\pi/10^7$ henrys per metre (H/m) is the absolute permeability of free space, and μ_r (numeric) is the relative, and μ the absolute permeability of the material.

We also have $B = \mu_o H + J$ where J is the intensity of magnetization in the specimen.

Fig. 1–1 shows, on suitable scales of H, the lower and upper parts of the initial magnetization curve of a sample of ordinary dynamo iron, which we may take to be representative in form of that for any ferromagnetic. The slope of the curve at the origin gives the initial relative permeability μ_{r1}, and the slope of the tangent to the curve the maximum value μ_{rm}. J approaches a saturation valve J_s at high field strengths, and if the scale of H enables this approach to saturation to be plotted, as in the upper curves, a fairly well-defined knee point appears at which it is evident that a change in the mechanism of the magnetization

1

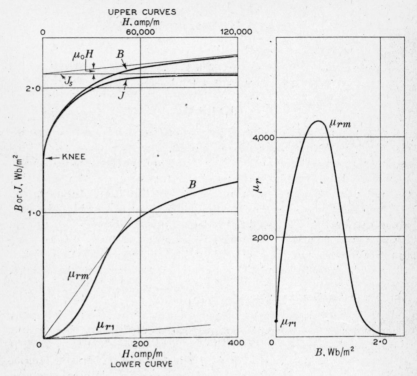

Fig. 1–1.—INITIAL MAGNETIZATION CURVE AND PERMEABILITY OF DYNAMO
IRON SHEET.

process occurs. The quantities μ_{r1}, μ_{rm}, J_s and sometimes the
position of the knee are important quantities in assessing magnetic
quality.

Magnetic Hysteresis

Fig. 1–2 shows the cyclic hysteresis loops obtained for a slowly
alternating applied field : (a), (b) and (c) are for a 4 per cent.
silicon-iron transformer sheet material for different peak values,
B_{max}, of the induction. The positive tips of the loops will lie on
the initial magnetization curve, while the area of the loops is a
measure of the energy dissipated in heat as a hysteresis loss per
unit volume, w_h, for each complete cycle. For any alternating
frequency, f, the specific energy loss, in watts per kilogramme, is :

$$W_h = \frac{f \cdot w_h}{\delta} \quad . \quad . \quad . \quad . \quad . \quad . \quad (1)$$

where δ is the density of the material (kg/m³). For a given B_{max} in a specimen w_h is not, in general, a constant, but almost certainly increases with increasing frequency (see also p. 6).

Curves (a), (b) and (c) are for a soft magnetic material, that is one in which the lowest hysteresis effect is desired. Curve (d) has been included for comparison, in particular, of the relative values of H. This is for a permanent magnet material (Alcomax II) in which the fullest possible hysteresis loop is aimed at.

The form of the relation between w_h and J_{max} when the alternating hysteresis cycle is made slowly is shown in Fig. 1–3 at (a). The particular values given are for a sample of silicon-iron sheet with 1·91 per cent. silicon. As may be seen from Fig. 1–1, B_{max} and J_{max} will be inappreciably different except at high flux densities. For $B_{max} < \frac{1}{2}J_s$ the Steinmetz empirical law, $w_h = \eta B_{max}^n$, fits the observed results fairly well, where η is the Steinmetz coefficient for the particular curve and the exponent n varies from about 1·6 to 1·8 for different materials. It will be seen, however, that there is a discontinuity in the curve occurring near the knee-point already mentioned. Above this region a straight line of the form

$$w_h = b(J_{max} - c)$$

where b and c are constants, fits the observed results fairly well up to the highest density to which measurements have been made,[1] i.e. up to about $0·85J_s$. The form of the relation in the neighbourhood of saturation is not known (but see Reference 39).

In the armatures of rotating machines a complicated mixture of alternating hysteresis loss, w_h, and rotational hysteresis loss, w'_h, occurs. The latter arises when, instead of an alternating flux in one direction in a specimen, there is a constant flux density which rotates in one plane: w'_h is then the loss per unit mass for one complete, slow revolution, and its relation to the rotating intensity of magnetization, J, is as shown in Fig. 1–3 (b). This curve [2] has a knee-point discontinuity, rises to a maximum and falls towards zero as saturation is approached.

Eddy Current Losses

Further losses occur with alternating or rotating magnetization due to the induced eddy currents. They are kept small in practice by employing insulated laminations. If the non-linearity between

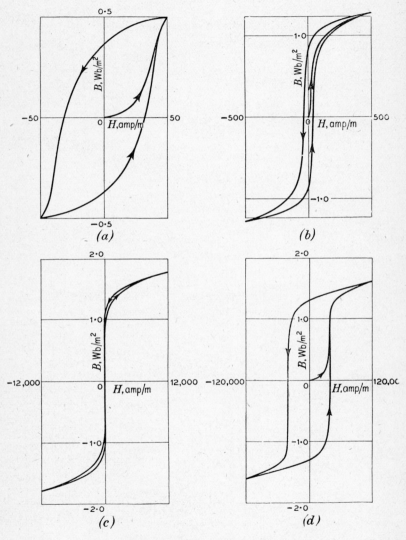

Fig. 1–2.—HYSTERESIS LOOPS.

(a), (b), (c) Soft magnetic material (4 per cent. silicon-iron). (d) Permanent magnet alloy (Alcomax II).

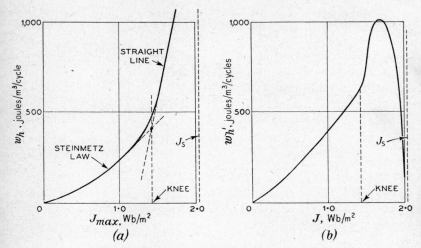

Fig. 1–3.—FORM OF HYSTERESIS LOSS CURVES.

(*a*) Alternating ; (*b*) rotational. Material : silicon-iron with 1·91 per cent. silicon.

B and H, to be seen in the hysteresis loops, is neglected and μ is assumed to be a constant, simple formulæ may be derived for sinusoidal conditions for the eddy losses in thick or thin plates.[3]

For alternating conditions in thick plates where $a\sqrt{\left(\dfrac{\mu f}{\pi\rho}\right)} > 1$, the eddy loss is given by

$$W_e = \frac{\sqrt{(\pi\mu f\rho)}}{2a \cdot \delta} \cdot H^2_{max} \quad \text{W/kg.}$$

$$= \frac{\sqrt{(\pi f\rho)} \cdot B^2_{max}}{2a \cdot \mu^{3/2}\delta} \quad \text{W/kg.}$$

where H_{max} and B_{max} are amplitudes at the sheet surface, $2a$ is the sheet thickness and ρ is the electrical resistivity.

For thin sheets where $a\sqrt{\left(\dfrac{\mu f}{\pi\rho}\right)}$ is small compared with unity,

$$W_e = \frac{(\pi \cdot 2a \cdot f \cdot B_{max})^2}{6 \cdot \rho \cdot \delta} \quad \text{W/kg.} \quad . \quad . \quad . \quad (2)$$

For a constant magnetic field H and flux density B rotating at a uniform speed of f revolutions per second, again neglecting complications introduced by hysteresis, the eddy-current losses will be precisely double the above values if we put B and H for B_{max} and H_{max} in the formulæ.

Total Iron Loss

The total specific iron loss W_t in a thin sheet under A.C. conditions will therefore be :

$$W_t = W_e + W_h \quad \text{W/kg.}$$

which, from equations (1) and (2), becomes at a given flux density :

$$\frac{W_t}{f} = k \cdot f + \frac{w_h}{\delta} \quad \text{J/kg./cycle}$$

where k is a constant.

The two parts of this expression are, respectively, the eddy current and hysteresis components of the total loss per cycle. It

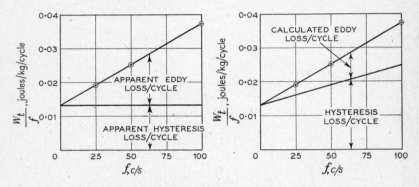

Fig. 1–4.—SEPARATION OF IRON LOSSES.

(Cold-reduced $3\frac{1}{4}$ per cent. silicon-iron sheet at $B_{max} = 1\cdot5$ Wb/m² observed points.)

has been common to assume that w_h is independent of frequency, making the relation between W_t/f and f a straight line from which an experimental separation of the losses could be made. This assumption, however, appears to be untenable. Fig. 1–4 shows, for example, some results obtained at three frequencies, at $B_{max} = 1\cdot5$ Wb/m², on a sample of cold-reduced $3\frac{1}{4}$ per cent. silicon-iron transformer sheet, 0·35 mm. thick. This material had unusually low hysteresis loss. On the left is the conventional method of loss separation. On the right is an alternative method which assumes the validity of equation (2). In this particular case the " apparent eddy loss " is about double the calculated value. The difference between these two quantities is sometimes called an " extra " or " anomalous loss." The evidence [4] indicates that it is due to a hysteresis effect and that the right-hand method of separation is, in fact, probably fairly accurate.

DOMAIN THEORY

Weber and Ewing considered that a ferromagnetic substance was made up of atomic or molecular magnets capable of rotation. The magnetic properties, according to Ewing, were determined by the magnetic forces between neighbouring magnets. The shape of magnetization curves and hysteresis loops could be explained in this way but quantitatively the theory fails completely to explain the high permeabilities observed with the ferromagnetics.

Modern Theory

In the modern theory the atoms or molecules of every paramagnetic or ferromagnetic material have, as in the older ideas, a magnetic moment. Fig. 1–5 represents, diagrammatically, a free atom of iron, with 26 orbital electrons situated in the main shells K, L, M and N about the central nucleus. Each electron is regarded as spinning gyroscopically on its own axis, by virtue of which and the negative charge which it carries, it is equivalent to a current in a small circular path. It therefore has a magnetic moment of unit amount equal to one Bohr magneton. Indepen-

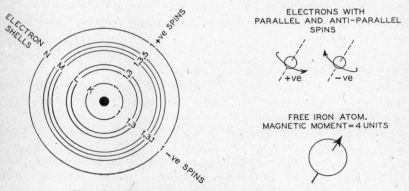

Fig. 1–5.—SPINNING ELECTRONS IN THE IRON ATOM.

dent evidence indicates that in a free iron atom there would be 15 electrons with parallel spins about a particular axial direction while the remaining 11 spin in the opposite direction. The figure indicates that all the atomic sub-shells are magnetically neutral except the incompleted outer one of shell M. In this there are four uncompensated spins which give the atom as a whole a magnetic moment of four units. Cobalt with one more orbital electron than iron has $+ 5$ and $- 2$ spins in this sub-shell, and nickel $+ 5$ and $- 3$. The free atoms of cobalt and nickel therefore have magnetic moments of 3 and 2 magnetons respectively.

However, the foregoing applies to hypothetical free atoms, and when these come together in the metallic state the distribution of the electrons in the outer shells is somewhat modified, giving average magnetic moments for iron, cobalt and nickel of 2·22, 1·71 and 0·606 units per atom respectively.

The Langevin-Weiss Theory

We suppose now that a magnetic field is applied in a particular direction to a substance, at room temperature, whose atoms or molecules each have a magnetic moment and are free to turn in any direction. Mutual magnetic effects between them of the kind envisaged in Ewing's theory will be small and may be neglected. However, there will be a tendency for the atomic magnetic axes to align themselves in the direction of the field, thus giving a resultant intensity of magnetization in that direction. This process is, however, so very strongly disturbed by the thermal motions of the atoms that the magnetic effect is, indeed, very feeble. Langevin [5] derived an expression for this case, which was later modified by the assumptions of quantum mechanics, to give the following :

$$\frac{J}{J_o} = \tanh \frac{vH}{kT} \quad \ldots \ldots \ldots \quad (3)$$

In this J is the intensity of magnetization produced by the field H. J_o is the value of J corresponding to parallel alignment of all the magnetic axes, v is the magnetic moment of each atom or molecule, T is the absolute temperature and k is Boltzmann's universal gas constant.

The Langevin theory is adequate for the paramagnetics, but fails when applied to the ferromagnetics, as we may see, for example, by substituting in equation (3) the appropriate values

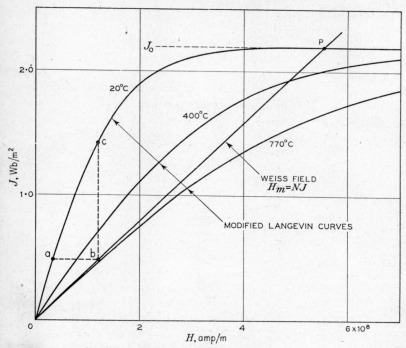

Fig. 1–6.—LANGEVIN MAGNETIZATION CURVES FOR IRON AT DIFFERENT TEMPERA-
TURES, AND WEISS MOLECULAR FIELD LINE.

for iron. For iron, in the m.k.s. system we have $J_o = 2.19$ Wb/m², $v = 2.56 \times 10^{-29}$ Wb-m, $k = 1.37 \times 10^{-23}$ J/°K, and at 20° C., $T = 293°$ K., and hence

$$J = 2.19 \cdot \tanh \frac{6.38H}{10^9} \text{ Wb/m}^2$$

The magnetization curve given by this expression is plotted in Fig. 1–6, from which it may be seen that saturation is approached only for fields of the order of 4×10^8 A/m, a figure which, compared with experimental observations on iron, is too high by a factor of about 10^4.

Weiss,[6] however, extended the Langevin theory to ferromagnetism. He assumed that in any ferromagnetic there existed a " molecular field " which was proportional in magnitude to the intensity of magnetization in the material, i.e. the molecular field

$H_m = NJ$ where N is a constant. We may represent this relation by the straight line OP shown in Fig. 1–6. If the slope of this line is less than the initial slope of the magnetization curve calculated from the Langevin theory, the material would be unstable in the unmagnetized condition at O. For suppose the material were accidentally magnetized by a small amount to a point a. This magnetization would automatically produce the molecular field corresponding to the point b, which by the Langevin theory would produce magnetization in the material corresponding to c, and so on until the point P was reached. The material would thus spontaneously magnetize itself to a saturation value J_s, a little lower than J_o, as indicated for a temperature of 20° C. by the point P.

Experimental Results

The Weiss theory has been amply confirmed by experiment and the origin of the powerful molecular field has been found [7] by the mathematicians. It is due to quantum-mechanical forces of interaction between neighbouring spinning electrons in the metal, which may be expected to produce nearly parallel alignment of the spins and hence spontaneous saturation in the elements iron, cobalt, nickel and gadolinium.[8] (The latter is a rare element which is ferromagnetic at temperatures below 16° C.).

From experimental results a value can be assigned to the constant N, and in Fig. 1–6 the straight line OP has been put in at the correct slope for iron. From equation (3) the Langevin curves corresponding to temperatures of 400° and 770° C. have also been drawn. It is clear that the intersection of the straight line and the curves gives the saturation values corresponding to the different temperatures. We can in fact derive the following relation :

$$\frac{J_s}{J_o} = \tanh\left(\frac{J_s}{J_o} \cdot \frac{\theta}{T}\right) \quad \cdots \quad \cdots \quad \cdots \quad (4)$$

where J_s is the saturation value for absolute temperature T and where $\theta = \dfrac{vNJ_o}{k}$.

From equation (4) we see that when $T = \theta$, $J_s = 0$. The relation between J_s and T for iron is plotted in Fig. 1–7. It will be seen that the saturation value falls with increasing temperature,

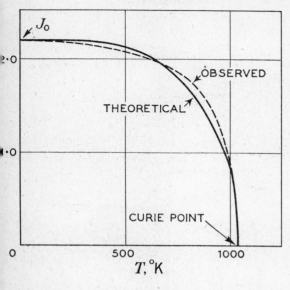

Fig. 1–7.—CALCULATED AND OBSERVED SATURATION OF IRON.

becoming zero at $\theta = 1043°$ K. (770° C.) for iron. Then θ is the magnetic change, or Curie point, and is the temperature at which a material changes from the ferromagnetic to the paramagnetic condition. The broken line indicates the experimentally observed saturation values for iron in fair agreement with the theory. Similar results are obtained for cobalt and nickel.

Domains and Crystals

The theory thus far indicates that any ferromagnetic material is spontaneously magnetized to saturation, even in the absence of an externally applied field, and we have therefore to account for the material in the apparently unmagnetized or partially magnetized condition. Weiss made a second postulate that the material was divided up into small volumes, called domains, each of which was saturated in a particular direction but that, for material in the technically demagnetized condition, these directions in neighbouring domains varied at random. Thus on applying a field a resultant magnetization in the field direction occurred due mainly to the domain vectors redirecting themselves in whole domains, this process requiring a much smaller applied field than in the case of a paramagnetic.

B 2

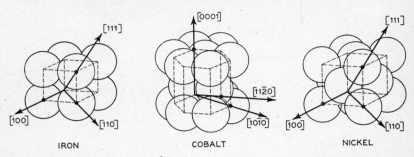

Fig. 1–8.—CRYSTAL STRUCTURES OF IRON, COBALT AND NICKEL, SHOWING ALSO THE MILLER INDICES.

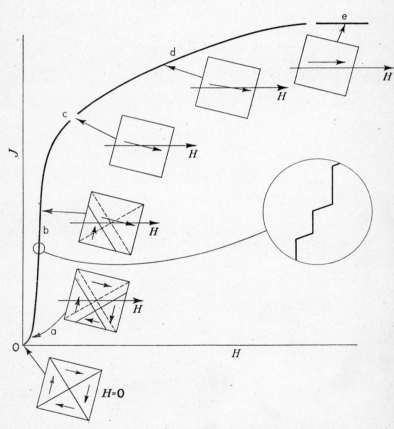

Fig. 1–9.—MAGNETIZATION PROCESSES IN AN IRON-TYPE CRYSTAL.

Now metals are crystalline substances. The crystal structures of iron, cobalt and nickel are shown in Fig. 1–8. Iron crystallizes on a body-centred cubic lattice, nickel is face-centred whilst cobalt takes a hexagonal form. In general, with no applied field a single domain will be part of a crystal in a polycrystalline material but will contain a very large number of atoms. Earlier experiments indicated that in ordinary polycrystalline materials the domains varied in size, containing up to 10^{15} atoms. However, recent work shows that domains may also be very much larger than this. In iron it is found that the direction of the spontaneous magnetization of the domain will be, without preference, along any one of the cube-edge directions of the crystal and a force is required to turn the magnetic axis away from this position. In nickel the equilibrium position is along a long diagonal of the crystal, and in cobalt along the longitudinal axis.

We may now consider the magnetization process for a ferromagnetic of the iron type by referring to Fig. 1–9. The squares represent a part of a single crystal, the edges corresponding to the cube edge directions of the crystal. This is shown divided up, at first, into four equal domains magnetically saturated in the directions of the arrows. There would be six possible directions for these arrows, but four only are shown for the purpose of this diagram. Initially the resultant magnetization in any direction is zero, corresponding to the point O of the magnetization curve. Suppose now a small field H is applied at an angle to a cube edge as shown. The first effect is that the boundaries between the domains move so as to increase the volume of the domains having a component of magnetization in the field direction and to decrease the others. The initial, almost reversible, part of the magnetization curve shown at a is thus obtained. When H is further increased some of the oppositely directed domains become unstable and the magnetization in these suddenly swings through $90°$ or $180°$. This occurs on the steeply rising part of the curve shown at b. An enlargement of this part of the characteristic would therefore show discrete steps, or Barkhausen jumps, as indicated in the circle. At c the latter process is complete and the magnetization in all the domains lies along the cube-edge nearest to the direction of H. This is the knee of the curve. Beyond c, a further increase in magnetization can occur only by a reversible turning of the domain vectors out of the cube edge direction into that of the field. This is found to require a field strength of a higher order than is needed below the point c (see Fig. 1–1) and gives the part d of the curve. Eventually this process is complete and technical saturation of the material results, as shown by the part e.

Large single crystals of iron, cobalt, nickel and a number of their alloys have been grown and the magnetization curves in different crystallographic directions determined.[9] The curves for iron are shown in Fig. 1–10 for three directions, denoted by the Miller indices [100], etc. (see Fig. 1–8). It will be seen that the cube edge is a direction of easy magnetization, whilst, for the [110] and [111] directions, there is a knee near $J_s/\sqrt{2}$ and $J_s/\sqrt{3}$, respectively, as we might expect from the theory and from the

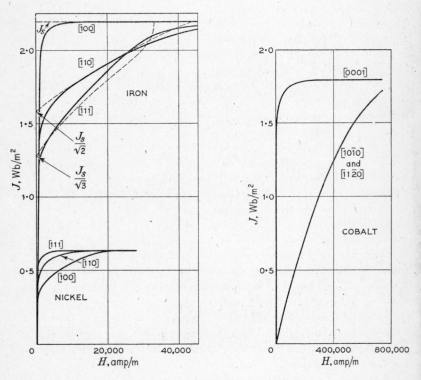

Fig. 1–10.—MAGNETIZATION CURVES FOR SINGLE CRYSTALS OF IRON, COBALT AND NICKEL. (The broken lines are theoretical.)

geometry of the crystal. Results for cobalt and nickel are also shown.

Experimental Confirmation

The existence of ferromagnetic domains has been well established by a variety of experiments, and there is a technique by which the domain boundaries, at the metal surface, can be made visible under the microscope. The metal surface is electrolytically polished and a soap solution containing a fine precipitate of magnetic iron oxide (Fe_3O_4) is applied. The magnetic particles collect at the domain boundaries, which may thus be examined. The resulting patterns are complicated and difficult to interpret. The simplest are for crystals of the iron type, where the surface being examined is slightly inclined to a cube-face plane of the crystal.[10] It is concluded from the observations, in confirmation of theoretical work by Néel,[11] that the domains in this case are narrow plates with short " closure " domains to form, in the absence of an applied field, small closed magnetic circuits in the material. This is illustrated in Fig. 1–11, from which it is seen that, for iron, the domain boundaries are parallel to cube faces, the angle between the domain vectors being 180° on either side of the boundary. Alternatively, at the ends of the plates, the domain boundary surfaces are at 45° to cube-face planes, the domain

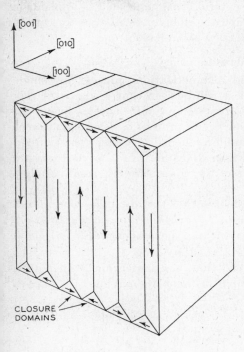

[001]
[010]
[100]

CLOSURE
DOMAINS

Fig. 1–11.—PROBABLE ARRANGE-
MENT OF DOMAINS IN AN IRON
CRYSTAL WITH NO APPLIED
FIELD.

vectors being at 90° on either side. In the former case there is no normal component of magnetization across the boundary, and in the latter the normal component is constant across the surface. There is therefore, in either case, no free pole appearing at the boundary. This is one of the conditions required to make the energy of the whole arrangement of domains a minimum. Another is that, for iron, the vectors shall lie along cube-edge directions as indicated in the Figure. There will, however, also be energy associated with the boundaries themselves and with the magnetostriction of the material, matters which will be referred to in the following sections. Néel has shown that the total energy is a minimum, leading to a stable arrangement of the domains, for the configuration shown, where the width of the plate-like domains is proportional to the square root of their length. In single crystals of 3·8 per cent. silicon-iron, Williams, Bozorth and Shockley have found domain widths of the order of 0·1 mm, although wide variations in domain dimensions are possible. They have also given results to show that the boundaries move, when an external magnetic field is applied, in the expected manner, to widen the domains whose vectors are in the field direction and to contract the adjacent ones.

The Upper Part of the Magnetization Curve

Considering the observed magnetization curves for single crystals of iron in Fig. 1–10, it will be seen that a comparatively small field in a cube edge direction is sufficient to bring the material almost to saturation. The process of magnetization is mainly one which involves sudden reversals or swings through 90° of the domain vectors in whole domains. In a perfect crystal saturation might be expected for a vanishingly small applied field.

However, for the field applied in the [110] direction the process just mentioned would be complete when the domain vectors were all at 45° to the field direction and the magnetization resolved into the field direction would then be $J_s/\sqrt{2}$. This gives the knee point beyond which the bulk magnetization J increases, not by sudden changes in direction of the domain but by a smooth rotational process.

Similarly for the [111] direction the knee point will be at $J_s/\sqrt{3}$ followed by a slow increase in J.

Theoretical expressions may be derived for these curves.[12]

If, in a saturated cubic crystal, the saturation vector J_s is in any position relative to the cube edges there will be crystalline forces acting to restore J_s, in the case of iron, to a cube-edge direction. There is therefore energy stored in the crystal on this account and, for cubic symmetry, this is given, very nearly, by

$$E = K_0 + K_1 (S_1{}^2 S_2{}^2 + S_2{}^2 S_3{}^2 + S_3{}^2 S_1{}^2) + K_2 (S_1 S_2 S_3)^2 \quad . \quad . \quad (5)$$

where K_0, K_1 and K_2 are constants and S_1, S_2 and S_3 are the direction cosines of J_s relative to the cube edges as co-ordinate axes. If now in a domain forming part of an iron crystal a field H is applied in the diagonal direction shown in Fig. 1–12, resulting in a rotation through an angle α of the saturation vector J_s, then it may be shown that J_s moves in the plane of the cube face and

$$E = K_0 + \frac{K_1}{8} (1 - \cos 4\alpha).$$

Apart from this magneto-crystalline energy there is also, due to the presence of J_s in the field H, potential energy

$$- HJ_s \cos \left(\frac{\pi}{4} - \alpha \right).$$

The total energy $E_T = K_0 + \dfrac{K_1}{8} (1 - \cos 4\alpha) - HJ_s \cos \left(\dfrac{\pi}{4} - \alpha \right)$.

The value of α which makes E_T a minimum, determined from

$$\frac{dE_T}{d\alpha} = 0 \quad . \quad . \quad . \quad . \quad . \quad . \quad . \quad (6)$$

gives the stable position of J_s.

The magnetization in the field direction is

$$J = J_s \cos \left(\frac{\pi}{4} - \alpha \right) \quad . \quad . \quad . \quad (7)$$

Elimination of α between equations (6) and (7) then gives the expression

$$H = \frac{2K_1}{J_s} \cdot \frac{J}{J_s} \left\{ 2 \left(\frac{J}{J_s} \right)^2 - 1 \right\} \quad . \quad . \quad (8)$$

which represents the magnetization curve for the [110] direction.

Similarly an expression, which is, however, somewhat lengthy, may be derived for the [111] direction, this including the constant K_2 also.

Using the values $K_1 = 4\cdot5 \times 10^4$, $K_2 = 2\cdot25 \times 10^4$ J/m³ and $J_s = 2\cdot16$ Wb/m², these expressions are plotted by the broken lines in Fig. 1–10 and show reasonably good agreement with the experimental results.

Nickel may be dealt with similarly, using appropriate values of K_1 and K_2. On the other hand, hexagonal cobalt requires the expression

$$E = K_0 + K_1 S_1{}^2$$

for the magnetocrystalline energy where S_1 is the direction cosine of J_s relative to the principal axis.

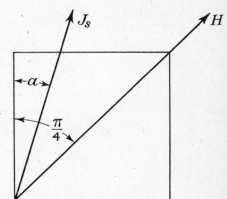

Fig. 1–12.—ROTATION PROCESS IN A DOMAIN OF IRON.

Domain Boundaries

Inside a domain the forces of interaction between neighbouring electron spins produce, in effect, the powerful Weiss molecular field, which acts to produce spontaneous saturation as already described. To rotate the axes of the atomic magnetic moments out of this position in the presence of the field would require energy which, for a reversal, would amount to $H_w J_s$ per unit volume where H_w is the Weiss field. On either side of a domain boundary, however, there will be an angle of either 90° or 180° between the respective spins, and this involves stored energy at the boundary. Bloch has shown [13] that as a result of this, in combination with the magnetocrystalline energy represented by equation (5), there is a gradual, rather than a sudden, transition in the angular position of the electron spins across the boundary which therefore has a substantial thickness.

A 180° boundary layer, or Bloch wall, is shown diagrammatically in Fig. 1–13. Such a layer in iron would, according to Stoner and Wohlfarth,[14] have a thickness of about 8.4×10^{-6} cm, corresponding to about 600 parallel layers of atoms, with energy stored amounting to 0.84×10^{-3} J/m³.

Magnetization in Comparatively Low Fields

The magnetic quality of a ferromagnetic material depends upon the ease or otherwise with which domain boundaries can move when a magnetic field is applied. This in turn depends upon internal strains in the material and upon that property of ferromagnetics, known as magnetostriction, whereby the material changes its dimensions when its state of magnetization is changed. The dimensional changes occurring are small but none the less of the greatest theoretical importance. Fig. 1–14 shows how the length of an iron crystal changes in the field direction when magnetized along different crystallographic axes.[15] Nickel and cobalt, on the other hand, contract when magnetized in any direction. It is known that internal strains, or crystal lattice distortions from other causes, also have a profound effect ; for example, a material in the hard, cold-worked condition has

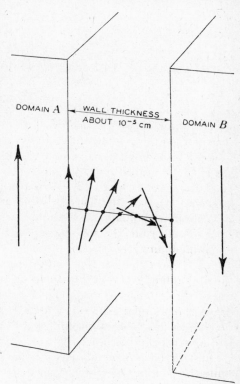

Fig. 1–13.—SHOWING GRADUAL CHANGE IN DIRECTION OF MAGNETIC MOMENTS ACROSS THE BOUNDARY BETWEEN TWO DOMAINS.

DOMAIN *A*

WALL THICKNESS ABOUT 10^{-5} cm

DOMAIN *B*

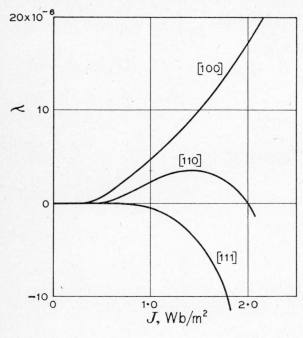

Fig. 1–14.—MAGNETO-
STRICTION   λ   OF
SINGLE CRYSTALS OF
IRON.

λ is the increase in
length per unit length.

a very much lower permeability and higher hysteresis loss than
the same material which has had the cold-working strains relieved
by heat-treatment (for example see Fig. 1–16).

Becker [16] and Kersten [17] have shown how to relate the permeability and coercivity with the magnetostriction and the
internal stresses. Becker considered an iron-type crystal, with
90° domain boundaries, having an idealized distribution of
compressive and tensile stress. The equilibrium positions of
domain boundaries with no applied field are at positions of zero
stress. As the field increases the boundaries move reversibly until
the boundary reaches a position of maximum stress when a sudden
irreversible jump occurs. On the other hand, with 180° boundaries the boundary, having a finite thickness as already described,
reaches an unstable position and jumps forward where the stress
gradient is a maximum.

On this basis the following expression, in rationalized m.k.s.
units, for the initial relative permeability may be obtained :

$$\mu_{r1} = \frac{2J_s^2}{3\pi\mu_0\lambda_s p}$$

where λ_s is the saturation magnetostriction along [100] and p is the amplitude of the internal stress. For a pure, well-annealed material in which all internal strains have been removed except those unavoidably present due to magnetostriction, this becomes

$$\mu_{r1} = \frac{2J_s^2}{3\pi\mu_0 \cdot \lambda_s^2 \cdot E} \quad \cdots \cdots \quad (9)$$

where E is Young's modulus, and this formula represents the highest value of initial permeability to be expected.

Somewhat similarly Kersten derives an expression for coercivity of the form

$$H_c = \frac{3}{2} \frac{\lambda_s p}{J_s} \quad \cdots \cdots \cdots \quad (10)$$

where p again denotes the internal stress amplitude.

The formulæ indicate that low values of magnetostriction and internal stresses will give a high permeability and low coercivity. Since the initial magnetization curve lies closely inside the hysteresis loop this condition also corresponds to a low hysteresis loss.

λ_s can be changed by alloying. Fig. 1–15 shows, in curve (a), how it varies with the nickel content in a series of nickel-iron alloys. Curve (b) shows observed values of μ_{r1} for air-quenched alloys [18] whilst (c) is derived from equation (9) above. At about 81 per cent. nickel $\lambda_s = 0$, and therefore μ_{r1} theoretically rises to infinity. However, the similarity between curves (b) and (c) is striking and in confirmation of Becker's theory.

The Problem of High Coercivity

In the permanent-magnet materials the characteristic of practical importance is the demagnetization curve, examples of which are shown in Fig. 1–24. This curve is a part of the hysteresis loop for saturation. The maximum hysteresis effect is desired in this case. In recent years materials of very high coercivity have been produced and the theoretical problem is to find a mechanism which will explain the high values observed.

The earlier permanent-magnet materials were martensitic steels depending upon the carbon present to introduce, after appropriate heat-treatment, high internal strains and so high mechanical and magnetic hardness. These materials had coercivities up to about 20,000 A/m. They were followed by the dispersion-hardened alloys having coercivities up to 70,000 A/m.

These high values of coercivity can hardly be accounted for by the Becker-Kersten mechanism. For if, in equation (10), we take $\lambda_s = 20 \times 10^{-6}$ and $J_s = 1\cdot5$ Wb/m^2, and further, let $p = 1\cdot5 \times 10^9$ newtons/m^2 (97 tons/in.^{2}), which is as high as or higher than the probable ultimate tensile strength of the material, we have $H_c = 30,000$ A/m. The theory might therefore embrace the martensitic steels but not the later materials. A later idea of Kersten's, the foreign-body theory, appears to have an even more limited application.

High coercivity is, moreover, not always accompanied by high internal strains. There are, for example, certain copper-nickel-

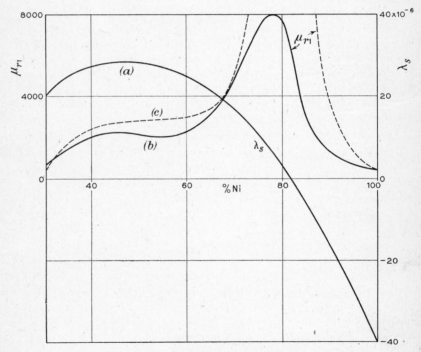

Fig. 1–15.—INITIAL PERMEABILITY AND SATURATION MAGNETOSTRICTION OF NICKEL-IRON ALLOYS.

iron alloys having coercivities up to about 40,000 A/m which are, at the same time, ductile, malleable and machinable.[19] It is reported that coercivities of over 30,000 A/m may be obtained, without heat-treatment, from compressed, commercially pure iron powder provided that the particles are below about 10^{-7} cm. in diameter.[20] This iron in the ordinary solid form would have a coercivity of only about 100 A/m. Again, as a matter of theoretical interest, very high coercivities have been observed [21] in materials, such as brass, containing ferromagnetic impurities, although in this case the retentivity would be exceedingly low.

Stoner and Wohlfarth [14] have shown theoretically how, in a very simple and probable way, values of coercivity of the order of those experimentally observed, and even much higher, could be accounted for. Néel has independently and similarly discussed the same problem. The material is considered to consist of fine ferromagnetic particles embedded in a dissimilar matrix. This might therefore well apply to the powdered-iron magnets, to such instances as brass containing iron as an impurity, and also to the dispersion-hardened alloys where one highly ferromagnetic phase may be in a particular state of precipitation from a magnetically dissimilar one.

It may be shown that if a ferromagnetic particle is below a certain critical size it will be a single domain. For if a particle is a single domain it will have energy stored on account of its spontaneous magnetization and its self-demagnetizing field. If the particle divides into two domains with a 180° boundary this energy vanishes but there is then energy stored due to the domain boundary wall as described on p. 18. Calculation shows that the latter energy is greater than the former in particles below a certain size which will therefore be, on this account, single domains. Stoner and Wohlfarth calculate that for spherical iron particles the critical diameter will be about 1.5×10^{-6} cm.

For single domain particles in the form of prolate spheroids it may then be shown that the field required to produce reversals of the magnetization in the particles, which we may take to be the coercivity, is given by

$$H_c = \frac{J_s}{2}(N_b - N_a)$$

where N_a and N_b are, respectively, the polar and equatorial demagnetizing factors of the prolate spheroid. H_c will be a high value even if the particle departs only by a small amount from the spherical form : for example, if the ratio of the polar to equatorial axes is 1·1 then, for iron, H_c would be about 60,000 A/m. Higher values would be obtained with more elongated particles, the limiting value for iron being about 800,000 A/m.

Strong support for the theory is given by some published results [20] on powdered iron magnets. A coercivity of 34,000 A/m is quoted for a particle size of 10^{-7} cm., but only 800 A/m for the same material with a particle size of 5×10^{-6} cm. Stoner and Wohlfarth's theory would, indeed, hold only for particles below the calculated, critical diameter of $1·5 \times 10^{-6}$ cm.

TECHNOLOGICAL ASPECTS

IT will be clear from the preceding that a requirement for high permeability and low hysteresis loss in a particular material is that the material shall be as free as possible from internal strains. Careful annealing of the metal is therefore necessary. Fig. 1–16 shows, for example, magnetization and rotational hysteresis loss curves for a sample of 4 per cent. silicon-iron in the annealed and cold-worked conditions respectively.[22]

Internal Strains and Impurities

A further important source of internal strains results from impurities, held either in solution or as larger inclusions in the metal. Yensen has made an extensive study of the effect of small amounts of the common impurities in iron and silicon-iron.[23] Carbon is particularly harmful, as Fig. 1–17 shows. Cioffi reduced the impurities carbon, sulphur, oxygen and nitrogen, in small specimens of iron, to a few thousandths of 1 per cent. each, by heat-treatment at temperatures a little below the melting point in a hydrogen atmosphere.[24] This treatment raised the maximum relative permeability to 280,000, which is about forty times that of ordinary dynamo iron, and reduced the hysteresis loss to about one-twentieth of that of the commercial material. For a single-crystal specimen of iron similarly treated [25] a maximum relative permeability of 1,430,000 was obtained for a cube edge direction of the crystal. There are limits to the degree of chemical purity which can be expected in materials produced by commercial

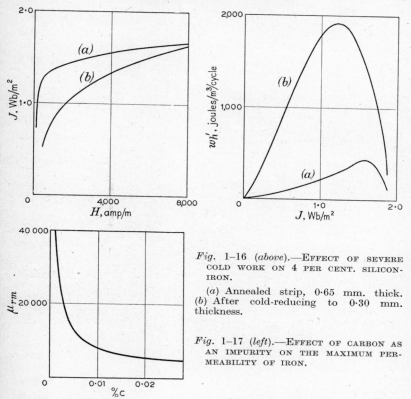

Fig. 1–16 (*above*).—Effect of severe cold work on 4 per cent. silicon-iron.

(*a*) Annealed strip, 0·65 mm. thick.
(*b*) After cold-reducing to 0·30 mm. thickness.

Fig. 1–17 (*left*).—Effect of carbon as an impurity on the maximum permeability of iron.

processes, rather than as small samples under laboratory conditions, but it is of interest to note that the material discussed in the next section is produced economically in large quantities with a carbon content of less than 0·005 per cent.

Preferred Orientation of Crystals

The iron and silicon-iron sheet materials used in electrical machinery and in transformers have, in the past, been produced by a hot-rolling process. Smith, Garnett and Randall, however, in experiments on nickel-iron alloys found that if the material was heavily cold-reduced in thickness, and annealed, greatly improved magnetic properties were obtained along the direction of rolling of the strip material.[26] Goss later described a cold-rolling procedure for silicon-iron, with silicon up to 3·5 per cent.,

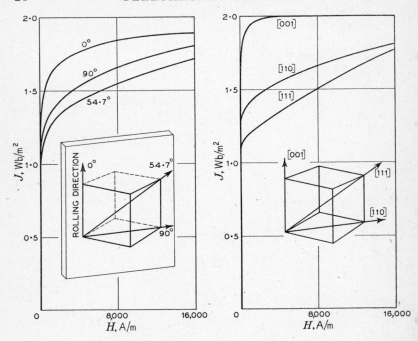

Fig. 1–18.—Directional magnetic properties of polycrystalline cold-
reduced 3 per cent. silicon-iron (*left*) and of single crystals of
3·85 per cent. silicon-iron (*right*).

which also resulted in a magnetically anisotropic sheet, the
direction of highest permeability and lowest hysteresis loss being
again in the rolling direction.[27] This material has been highly
developed and is now being produced on a large scale. It has
proved so greatly superior to the hot-rolled material that, in the
United States at least, the latter is being superseded by cold-
reduced steel for transformers and in turbo-alternators.

The directional properties of this material are due to the
constituent crystals in the sheet taking up a " preferred orientation." In silicon-iron the crystals are lined up, approximately,
with a cube edge direction in the direction of rolling and with the
diagonal [110] plane in the plane of the sheet. In the best material
almost the whole of the crystals are so arranged with, however, a
small spread about this position. The polycrystalline material
therefore has directional magnetic properties similar to those for

a single crystal. Fig. 1–18 shows, for example, a comparison between the magnetization curves of an early sample of Goss sheet and a 3·85 per cent. silicon-iron single crystal,[28] while Fig. 1–19 shows curves of hysteresis loss in the sheet [1] and in a 2·1 per cent. silicon-iron single crystal.[29]

A useful method [2] of estimating the degree of preferred orientation in a specimen of the cold-reduced sheet is to cut a disc from it, and to measure the torque required to rotate it slowly in a strong magnetic field which is in the plane of the disc. Such a disc, if cut from the diagonal [110] plane of a cubic crystal, may be shown by making use of equation (5), page 17, to require the following torque per unit volume :

$$L = - \left(\frac{K_1}{4} + \frac{K_2}{64} \right) \sin 2\alpha - \left(\frac{3K_1}{8} + \frac{K_2}{16} \right) \sin 4\alpha + \frac{3K_2}{64} \sin 6\alpha.$$

This theoretical curve is shown at (a) in Fig. 1–20 for a $3\frac{1}{4}$ per cent. silicon-iron crystal. The observed curve at (b) was obtained for a disc cut from a polycrystalline, cold-reduced $3\frac{1}{4}$ per cent. silicon-iron sheet. The close resemblance in shape of the two curves will be noted. Comparison of their amplitudes indicates that about 80 per cent. of the crystals had the preferred orientation which

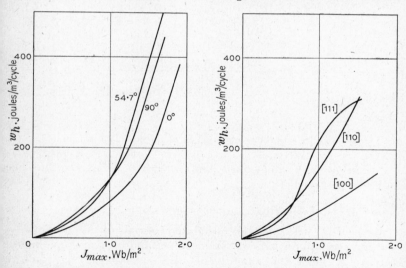

Fig. 1–19.—Alternating hysteresis loss in different directions in polycrystalline cold-reduced 3 per cent. silicon-iron (*left*) and in single crystals of 2·1 per cent. silicon-iron (*right*).

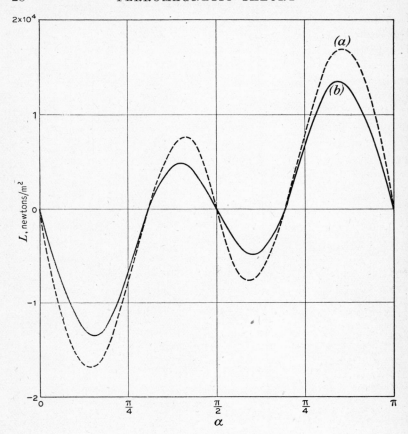

Fig. 1–20.—TORQUE CURVES.

(*a*) Theoretical for [110] plane of 3¼ per cent. Silicon iron single crystal.
(*b*) Observed for polycrystalline cold-reduced 3¼ per cent. silicon-iron disc.

has been already mentioned and is clearly illustrated in the
diagrams in Fig. 1–18.

Some Effects of Alloying

Silicon-iron with varying amounts of silicon is universally
used for the laminations of transformers and electrical machines.
Brittleness limits the amount of silicon that can be usefully
employed to about 5 per cent. Four per cent. silicon raises the
electrical resistivity of commercial iron by about four times and

therefore reduces eddy current losses in this inverse ratio. At the same time, probably because of the effect of silicon on the impurities present, and on the grain size, the hysteresis loss is reduced to about one-half. Aluminium behaves similarly and there is no other competitor, at least for materials for use in power plant.

However, a remarkable series of magnetic alloys is obtained by alloying iron and nickel together in different proportions. When the composition is near to Fe Ni_3 very high initial and maximum permeabilities are obtainable with very low hysteresis loss. This

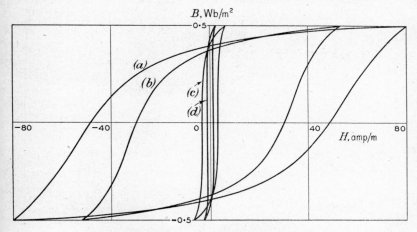

Fig. 1–21.—COMPARISON OF HYSTERESIS LOOPS.
(*a*) Dynamo iron ; (*b*) 4 per cent. silicon-iron ; (*c*) Mumetal ; (*d*) Supermalloy.

has already been discussed on p. 21. It may be noted that the initial relative permeability of dynamo iron is about 250, but nickel-iron alloys of about the composition mentioned have values of over 10,000 and, when great care is taken with the heat treatment, this figure is raised to about 100,000. A comparison of the hysteresis is given in Fig. 1–21 for (*a*) dynamo iron, (*b*) 4 per cent. silicon-iron transformer sheet, (*c*) Mumetal with a composition of 75 per cent. Ni, 16 per cent. Fe, 5 per cent. Cu and 4 per cent. Mo, and (*d*) carefully prepared Supermalloy [30] containing 79 per cent. Ni, 15 per cent. Fe, 5 per cent. Mo and 0.5 per cent. Mn.

These nickel-iron alloys are valuable in applications where

superior properties in weak fields are required. They are, however, too low in saturation value and too high in cost to be used in heavy electrical equipment. The way in which the saturation value [31] varies with the nickel content in iron is shown in Fig. 1–22. The corresponding curves for silicon in iron, and for cobalt in iron, are also shown. Cobalt it will be seen raises the saturation value to a maximum about 11 per cent. greater than that of iron. This higher saturation would be useful, for example, in the rotor punchings of electric motors, but the use of the alloys is

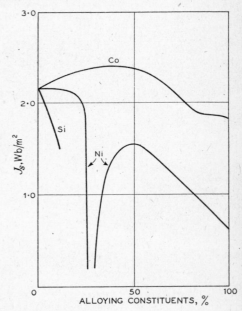

Fig. 1–22.—SATURATION VALUES OF SILICON-IRON, NICKEL-IRON AND COBALT-IRON ALLOYS.

limited because of the high cost of cobalt and the difficulty in rolling the alloy.

Heat Treatment in a Magnetic Field

It has been found with certain alloys that, if they are allowed to cool through the Curie point in the presence of an applied field, the materials at room temperature are magnetically anisotropic with improved properties in the selected direction. For soft magnetic materials this effect is greatest in nickel-iron with 65 to 70 per cent. nickel. Fig. 1–23 shows results obtained by Dillinger and Bozorth [32] for a specimen with 65 per cent. nickel. Curve (a) was for the material annealed in hydrogen at 1,400° C. Curve (b) shows the remarkable change in permeability occurring after heating the specimen to 650° C. for a few minutes in a magnetic field of 800 A/m. The domains form during cooling through the magnetic change point. The domain vectors and magneto-strictive expansion will be aligned by the field in one direction. If the temperature is high enough to allow strain relief in the metal during the subsequent cooling, the domain vectors will finally have one axial direction which is energetically preferred and which thus becomes a direction of easy magnetization.

It has been similarly found [33] that dispersion-hardened alloys of suitable composition can have their demagnetization charac-teristic greatly improved by applying during cooling a magnetic field some thirty times greater than the above. Fig. 1–24 shows curves for Alcomax, (a) for the direction selected during cooling, and (b) for a lateral direction. The possibility that, in this case, the material is made up of particles below the critical size, (see p. 23), whose shape during domain formation has been influenced by this treatment, and to which, therefore, Stoner and Wohlfarth's theory would apply, has been discussed by Hoselitz and McCaig.[34]

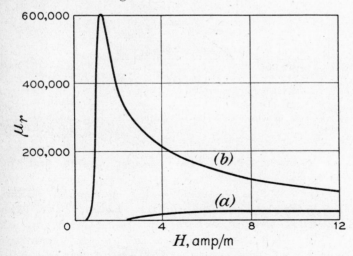

Fig. 1–23.—EFFECT OF ANNEALING IN A MAGNETIC FIELD ON A SAMPLE OF 65 PER CENT. NICKEL-IRON ALLOY.

Industrial Measurements

The precision measurement of the magnetization curve and hysteresis loop of a magnetic material may be done, for specimens in the form of straight strips or rods, in a permeameter of which several different types are in common use. These include the Illovici, the Fahy, the Webb and Ford, and the Burrows[35] and that described by Armour, King and Walley.[36]

The latter type is shown diagrammatically in Fig. 1–25. The

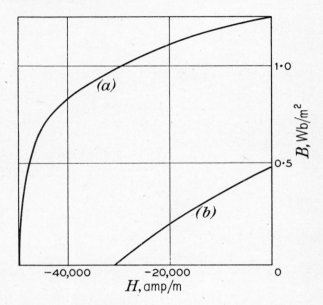

Fig. 1–24.—DEMAGNETIZATION CURVES OF ALCOMAX.

(*a*) In the direction in which the field was applied during cooling. (*b*) In a lateral direction.

specimen is magnetized by a heavy copper winding and the magnetic circuit is completed by a pair of heavy yokes. Extra windings are provided at the ends of the specimen to provide additional m.m.f. for the reluctance of the junction between the specimen and the yokes. By suitable adjustment of the currents in the main and compensating windings uniform field conditions are established, at least over the central part of the specimen. *H*-coils are provided near the specimen, and it is usual to measure

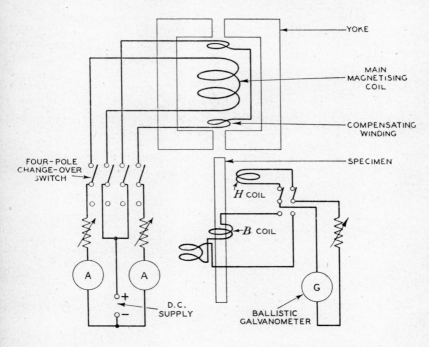

YOKE

MAIN
MAGNETISING
COIL

COMPENSATING
WINDING

SPECIMEN

FOUR-POLE
CHANGE-OVER
SWITCH

H COIL

B COIL

A   A

+

−

D.C.
SUPPLY

G

BALLISTIC
GALVANOMETER

Fig. 1–25 (*above*).—PERMEAMETER CIR-
CUIT ARRANGEMENT WITH SPECIMEN
REMOVED FROM YOKE.

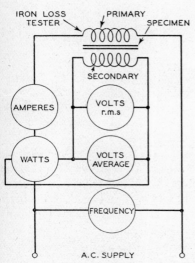

IRON LOSS
TESTER

PRIMARY

SPECIMEN

SECONDARY

AMPERES

VOLTS
r.m.s

WATTS

VOLTS
AVERAGE

FREQUENCY

A.C. SUPPLY

Fig. 1–26 (*left*).—CONNECTIONS FOR
IRON-LOSS TESTING.

$(B - \mu_0 H)$, or J, directly, employing a B-coil round the specimen and an H coil alongside of identical area-turns connected in opposition. When uniform conditions are established H may be determined from the ampere turns on the main magnetizing winding and J from the deflection of a ballistic galvanometer.

Iron-loss measurements at supply frequencies are normally made on a specimen built up to form a closed magnetic circuit. There are three types of tester recognized by the B.S.I.[37] : (a) the Lloyd-Fisher Square, (b) the Churcher tester, and (c) the Epstein

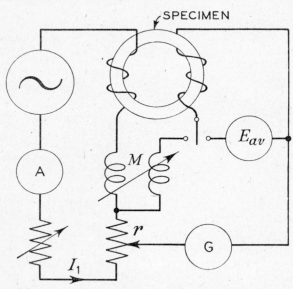

Fig. 1–27.—CAMPBELL A.C. POTENTIOMETER FOR IRON-LOSS TESTING.

Square. These differ mainly in the size and arrangement of the specimen. In the Lloyd-Fisher method thirty-two pieces, each 25×7 cm., are used. These are arranged on edge in four packs of eight, like the sides of a box, with small corner pieces to complete the circuit. The Churcher tester uses sixteen pieces each 30×4 in. in two packets of eight, the circuit being completed by U-shaped end pieces. The Epstein square has four equal packets of laminations with butt joints. In all cases the tester is provided with primary and secondary windings as shown diagrammatically in Fig. 1–26. With the circuit shown copper losses in the primary winding are not included in the wattmeter reading, but corrections must be made for instrument losses and for losses in the corner pieces. A dynamometer wattmeter is usually employed and, to determine B_{max}, the average voltage is observed using a moving-coil voltmeter in conjunction with a rectifier.

An alternative method of iron-loss measurement, which is convenient for flux densities up to about half the saturation value and for small specimens, is by means of an A.C. potentiometer. A form of this due to Campbell [38] is shown in Fig. 1–27. In this circuit a ring specimen is shown, with primary and secondary windings, excited by a sinusoidal current rather than with the sinusoidal flux which is aimed at in the preceding methods. The magnitude and phase angle of the secondary e.m.f. is measured in relation to the magnetizing current and hence the iron loss may be calculated. A balance is obtained by varying the mutual inductance M and the potentiometer resistance r. Then the iron loss in watts is given by

$$W = I_1{}^2 r (T_1/T_2),$$

the power factor by $\cos \phi = r/\sqrt{(r^2 + \omega^2 M^2)}$

and the flux density by $B_{max} = E_{av}/4faT_2$

where T_1 and T_2 are the primary and secondary turns respectively, I_1 is the primary r.m.s. current, $\omega = 2\pi f$, a is the cross-section of the specimen and E_{av} is the average value of the secondary e.m.f.

Various forms of A.C. bridge have been used for measurements under incremental conditions, that is when the specimen carries an alternating and a steady flux at the same time, and for measurements at audio and radio frequencies, but a fuller discussion of magnetic measurements is not possible here.

References

1. BRAILSFORD, F. *Journ. I.E.E.*, 1939, **84**, 399.
2. BRAILSFORD, F. *Journ. I.E.E.*, 1938, **83**, 566.
3. RUSSELL, A. " Alternating Currents," Vol. I, 1914.
4. STEWART, K. H. *Proc. I.E.E.*, 1950, Pt. II, **97**, 121.
5. LANGEVIN, P. *Ann. de Chim. et de Phys.*, 1905, (8), **5**, 70.
6. WEISS, P. *Journ. de Phys.*, 1907, (4), **6**, 661.
7. HEISENBERG, W. *Zeits. f. Phys.*, 1928, **49**, 619.
8. BETHE, H. *Handb. d. Phys.*, 1933, 24/2, 595.

9. HONDA, K., and KAYA, S.   *Sci. Rep. Toh. Imp. Univ.*, 1926, Series 1, 15, 721.
   KAYA, S.   *Sci. Rep. Toh. Imp. Univ.*, 1928, Series 1, 17, 639 and 1157.
10. WILLIAMS, H. J., BOZORTH, R. M., and SHOCKLEY, W.   *Phys. Rev.*, 1949, 75, No. 1, 155.
11. NEEL, L.   *Journ. de Phys.*, 1944, (8), 5, 241.
12. AKULOV, N. S.   *Zeits. f. Phys.*, 1929, 57, 249 ; 1931, 67, 794 ; 1931, 69, 78.
13. BLOCH, F.   *Zeits. f. Phys.*, 1932, 74, 295.
14. STONER, E. C., and WOHLFARTH, E. P.   *Phil. Trans. Roy. Soc.*, 1948, A, 240, 599.
15. WEBSTER, W. L.   *Proc. Roy. Soc.*, A, 1925, 109, 570.
16. BECKER, R.   *Zeits. f. Phys.*, 1930, 62, 253 ; *Phys. Zeits.*, 1932, 33, 905.
17. KERSTEN, M.   *Zeits. f. Phys.*, 1931, 71, 562 ; *Zeits. f. tech. Phys.*, 1938, 19, 546 ; *Electrotech. Zeits.*, 1939, 60, 498.
18. ELMEN, G. W.   *Journ. Frank. Inst.*, 1928, 206, 317 ; 1929, 207, 582.
19. DAHL, O., PFAFFENBERGER, J., and SCHWARTZ, N.   *Metallwirtschaft*, 1935, 14, 665.
   NEUMANN, H.   *Metallwirtschaft*, 1935, 14, 778.
   NEUMANN, H., BUCHNER, A., and REINBOTH, H.   *Zeits. f. Metallkunde*, 1937, 29, 173.
20. British Pat. Spec. 590,392.
21. SCHRÖDER, H.   *Ann. Phys.*, 1939, 36, 71.
   CONSTANT, F. W., and FORMWALT, J. M.   *Phys. Rev.*, 1939, 56, 373.
22. BRAILSFORD, F.   " Magnetic Materials," 1948.
23. YENSEN, T. D.   *Trans. Amer. I.E.E.*, 1924, 43, 145.
   YENSEN, T. D., and ZIEGLER, N. A.   *Trans. Amer. I.E.E.*, 1935, 23, 556 ; 1936, 24, 337.
24. CIOFFI, P. P.   *Phys. Rev.*, 1932, 39, 363 ; 1934, 45, 742.
25. CIOFFI, P. P., WILLIAMS, H. J., and BOZORTH, R. M.   *Phys. Rev.*, 1937, 51, 1009.
26. SMITH, W. S., GARNETT, H. J., and RANDALL, W. F.   Brit. Pat. Spec., 366, 523.
27. GOSS, N. P.   *Trans. Amer. Soc. Metals*, 1935, 23, 511 ; Brit. Pat. Spec. 442,211.
28. WILLIAMS, H. J.   *Phys. Rev.*, 1937, 52, 747.
29. WILSON, A. J. C.   *Proc. Phy. Soc.*, 1946, 58, 21.
30. BOOTHBY, O. L., and BOZORTH, R. M.   *Journ. App. Phys.*, 1947, 18, 173.
31. YENSEN, T. D.   *Trans. Amer. I.E.E.*, 1920, 39, 791.
32. DILLINGER, J. F., and BOZORTH, R. M.   *Physics*, 1935, 6, 279.
33. OLIVER, D. A., and SHEDDEN, J. W.   *Nature*, 1938, 142, 209.
   Brit. Pat. Spec., 522,731.
   VAN URK, A. T.   *Phillips Tech. Rev.*, 1940, 5, 29.
34. HOSELITZ, K., and McCAIG, M.   *Proc. Phy. Doc.*, B, 1949, 62, 163.
   HOSELITZ, K.   " Ferromagnetic Properties of Metals and Alloys," 1952.
35. ASTBURY, N. F.   " Industrial Magnetic Measurements," 1952.
36. ARMOUR, A. M., KING, A. J., and WALLEY, J. W.   *Proc. I.E.E.*, 1952, Pt. IV, 99, No. 2, 74.
37. B.S. 601. 1935.
38. CAMPBELL, A.   *Proc. Phys. Soc.*, 1920, 22, 232.
39. BRAILSFORD, F., and BRADSHAW, C. G.   *Nature*, 1953, 178, 35.

2. (a) SOFT MAGNETIC MATERIALS

By

W. S. MELVILLE, B.Sc.(Eng.), M.I.E.E.

MAGNETICALLY-SOFT materials constitute by far the major proportion of alloys and steels manufactured for use in electrical equipment. Although, by comparison with the vast quantities of structural steel produced, the total output of iron-based electrical alloys is small, nevertheless on the special properties of these alloys depends the economical functioning of almost all electrical installations.

The two principal fields of electrical engineering in which these alloys find application are :

(i) Rotating machines (both for electrical power generation and for motive power plants) and

(ii) Static power transformers (which are essential to the economical distribution and utilization of electrical energy).

In addition, there has grown up over the past twenty years a smaller, but in some respects even more important, application in the electronics and telecommunications industries. This field embraces industrial-process control, nuclear-particle accelerators, radar, radio, television, telephony and telegraphy, metering and protection, small rotating machines with special characteristics and a large and growing number of other applications. In many of these the quantity of alloy per unit is a tiny fraction of that required by a single larger power transformer, but the number of units constructed may be several tens of thousands. The total requirement in this field is thus by no means negligible. Alloys used for these applications frequently require to have magnetic properties of the highest-available quality, or special characteristics that demand that production processes be controlled with very great care.

Main Lines of Development

There are thus two main lines of development to be examined. The first has as its aim the production of large quantities of magnetic steel in which the cost of attaining low loss and good magnetic properties on a bulk manufacturing scale must be balanced against the long-range economic problems of the losses in power generation and distribution apparatus. The second is that in which the best possible magnetic properties for specific applications are required but in which, because of the comparatively small quantities involved, cost of production is relatively unimportant and can be subordinated to the over-riding considerations of characteristics and quality.

There is a further consideration : certain alloys exhibit their optimum properties only when used in particular physical relationships to the magnetic field in which they are operating. This imposes restrictions on their use which cannot always be reconciled with economic design of equipment. Other alloys, although magnetically advantageous, have mechanical characteristics (such as brittleness) which make it difficult to manufacture them in convenient shapes and therefore preclude their use in some kinds of apparatus.

These considerations are ever-present in the minds of manufacturers of magnetic alloys and designers of electrical equipment. Remarkable advances have been made in the development of new materials and alloys, and in adaptation and methods of construction to derive optimum benefit from the improved characteristics.

Efforts on the scientific side, aimed at a more comprehensive understanding of the fundamental physical process of magnetization, are continually making progress. With recent advances, particularly by Néel, Bozorth and Williams, this important subject, until comparatively recently largely empirical, is beginning to assume the status of an exact science. The extent to which these basic investigations, with their laboratory background of high purity, exact compositions and heat treatment, can be translated into technological practice on an industrial scale remains to be seen, but already the grain-oriented iron-silicon alloys and grain-and-domain-oriented nickel-iron alloys have progressed from the research stage to established production.

In order to make optimum use of the materials at his disposal, it is necessary for the electrical engineer and magnetic component designer to understand and appreciate their properties and limitations. He must also take into account the economics of their

Table 1. Properties of Ferro-magnetic Elements at Room Temperature

Element	Coercive Force (oersteds)	Initial Permeability	Max Permeability	* Saturation Induction (gauss)	Resistivity (microhm cm)
Iron	0·8 – 1·0	150 – 300	3000 – 10,000	21,580	9·7 – 11
Nickel	6	300	2,500	6,084	6·8
Cobalt	8 – 12	60 – 80	250	17,870	6·2

* For technically pure material

Table 2. Some Properties of Commercially-available Iron-nickel Alloys

Alloy Characteristic	Approx. % Ni	Commercial Name	Permeability Initial	Permeability Maximum	Saturation Induction gauss approx	Resistivity microhm. cm	Hysteresis Loss (B=5000 g) ergs per cc per cycle
High Initial Permeability	75 – 80	Mumetal	20,000 to 30,000	110,000	7,800	60	38·5
		Permalloy C	10,000 to 30,000	50,000 to 100,000	8,000	60	45
High Saturation Density	45 – 50	Radiometal	2000	20,000 to 25,000	16,000	40	218
		Permalloy B	18,000 to 2,400	10,000 to 20,000	16,000	55	300
High Resistivity	35 – 40	Rhometal	1000	10,000	12,000	95	438
		Permalloy D	1500 to 2000	6000 to 8000	13,000	90	550
Domain-Oriented (Rectangular loop)	65	Permalloy F	—	200,000 to 250,000	14,000	20	210 *
Grain & Domain-Oriented (Rectangular loop)	50	H.C.R metal	500 to 1000	200,000 to 250,000	16,000	40	570 *

* at saturation induction

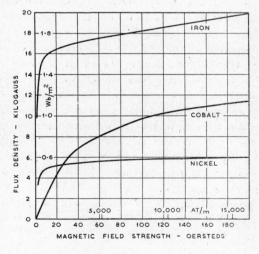

Fig. 2–1.—Typical Magnetization Curves of Commercially Pure Iron, Cobalt and Nickel.

manufacture and use so that equipment is designed by logical exploitation of the characteristics most suited to the electrical specification. The information given later in this chapter summarizes the important characteristics of commonly-used soft magnetic materials and indicates their fields of application.

Basic Soft Magnetic Materials

Before proceeding to the consideration of specific commercially-available materials, some general remarks on soft magnetic materials and factors affecting their properties may help to explain the limitations of the commercial products.

The three basic ferromagnetic elements are iron, cobalt and nickel. Of these, iron is by far the cheapest and most plentiful, but all three have important applications as alloying elements in soft magnetic materials. Typical magnetization curves for commercially-pure samples of these elements are shown in Fig. 2–1 and other relevant data are given in Table 1.

Iron

From these data it is seen that iron of high purity is in several respects a material with very good magnetic properties in its own right, and indeed when purified and refined under laboratory conditions its properties are among the best attained for any ferro-magnetic substance. For example, by prolonged refinement of iron in a hydrogen atmosphere at high temperature, Cioffi [1] has produced polycrystalline samples having initial permeabilities of 20,000–30,000 and maximum permeabilities of the order of 250,000, the corresponding coercive force being less than 4 AT/m (0·05 oersted). Bozorth [2] has recorded a maximum permeability of 1,400,000 for a single crystal of similarly purified iron magnetized in the easy direction along the cube edge. Unfortunately these superior properties are attainable only when extraordinary measures have been adopted to minimize the proportions of harmful impurities ; the total percentage in the cases quoted being about 0·03 per cent.

The enormous cost of producing material of this order of purity in commercially-useful quantities by vacuum-melting, high-temperature hydrogen annealing, or electrolysis, removes practical significance from such suggestions. It is also unfortunately true that the purification of iron to better than say 0·3 per cent. total impurities is difficult by commercially-economic processes and that at this figure the magnetic properties, both as regards loss and permeability, have deteriorated by some twenty to fifty times compared with those of technically-pure iron.

Effect of Impurities

The impurities principally responsible for this deterioration are carbon, sulphur, oxygen and nitrogen. The effects of these and other impurities on magnetic pro-perties have been investigated in great detail by Yensen [3, 4] both in pure iron and iron-silicon alloys ; Elmen [5] has done similar work on alloys of iron, cobalt and nickel.

In general, the best magnetic properties, as exemplified by low hysteresis loss and high perme-ability, are associated with a strain-free material having a regular crystal matrix and large grains. These conditions ensure that domain boundary movements can take place freely in response to externally applied fields. The presence of impurities adversely affects this freedom by causing strains and irregularities which impede movement and inhibit grain growth.

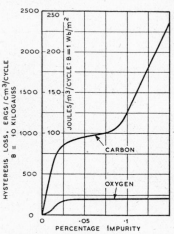

Fig. 2–2.—EFFECTS OF IMPURITIES ON HYSTERESIS LOSS IN IRON (YENSEN).

In solution, impurities can cause distortion of the crystal lattice by taking the place of atoms of the basic material ; they may also appear in solution at the interstices of the lattices of the basic material and cause severe local strains. When the impurities are present in quantities exceeding those supportable in solid solution, the formation of non-magnetic inclusions, precipitates and aggre-gates occurs throughout the material, and increase its magnetic hardness by strains due to deformation of the lattice structure in their vicinity. In addition such inclusions cause magnetic dilution of the material and reduce the effective saturation induc-tion ; they also decrease the effective permeability by local demagnetizations.

Some of Yensen's measurements of the effects of carbon and

oxygen on hysteresis loss in pure iron are shown in Fig. 2–2. The presence of sulphur is estimated to increase the hysteresis loss approximately linearly with increasing content to the extent of about 15 J/m³ or 150 ergs/cm³ per cycle per 0·01 per cent. sulphur. This element is harmful also in that hot working properties of the material are seriously impaired, causing difficulties in fabrication. Nitrogen has the effect of inhibiting grain growth.

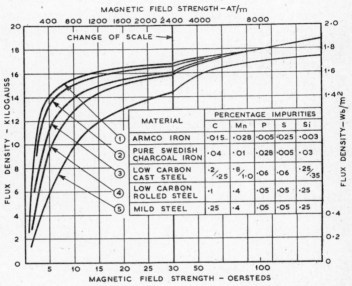

Fig. 2–3.—MAGNETIZATION CURVES FOR COMMON MAGNETIC STEELS AND IRONS.

From these data, it is evident that very small percentages of impurities can contribute very large factors to magnetic losses in iron. They have similar effects in other iron-based alloys.

Magnetic Ageing

Impurities are also the cause of the phenomenon known as magnetic ageing. In materials with excessive impurities this manifests itself as a gradual—and in some cases catastrophic—increase in the losses and magnetizing current under normal working conditions. In the early days of electrical engineering before the importance of high purity in magnetic materials was recognized, ageing was a common cause of plant failure. The phenomenon is now thought to be due to the precipitation of chemical compounds of iron, carbon, oxygen and nitrogen which are present in supersaturated solid solution in the basic material. The solubility of the impurities in the iron is greatly increased at the elevated temperatures employed in the processing of the material ; and on cooling, amounts of impurities in excess of the stable quantity are held in solid solution. This excess is gradually precipitated during normal life, causing severe strains in the crystal lattice with consequent increase in hysteresis losses and decrease in permeability. The effect is virtually eliminated if the percentage of impurities in the basic material is less than that which can be held in solid solution at normal working temperatures.

Low-carbon Steels

Modern low-carbon steels for magnetic purposes, such as those for which magnetization characteristics are shown in Fig. 2–3 (curves 1, 2, 3 and 4), have sufficient purity to reduce the effect to negligible proportions, but the most effective remedy has been achieved by alloying the iron with silicon. The silicon acts as a de-oxidizing agent and chemically reacts with any oxides present in the basic material to form silicates which are precipitated as slag ; in suitable proportions it also has the effect of causing carbon to be precipitated as graphite aggregates instead of as finely-dispersed cementite which is more harmful to magnetic properties. The iron-silicon alloys are discussed in detail later.

Soft Magnetic Alloys

The foregoing discussion of the magnetic properties of simple unalloyed iron have shown that provided such material can be obtained in sufficiently pure form it has considerable potential usefulness. For steady-flux applications such as machine frames, poles, yokes, and rotors, electro-magnet poles and yokes, relay cores and the like in which hysteresis and eddy current losses are immaterial, its high permeability and high saturation flux density are important advantages. Its low resistivity however proves to be a substantial drawback for A.C. applications in which cyclic magnetization produces losses due to eddy currents : in these applications such materials are restricted to cases in which high efficiency is less important than low cost, or where high saturation is essential.

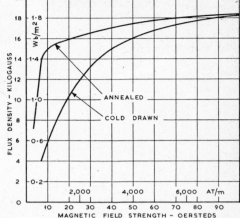

Fig. 2–4.—EFFECT OF ANNEALING ON STRAINED ARMCO INGOT IRON.

In view of these limitations, it is to be expected that a great deal of work has been done to determine whether alloys exist that have more suitable properties. At present, only four main groups of binary alloys have achieved practical significance and interest. These are :

Iron-silicon,
Iron-nickel,
Iron-cobalt and
Iron-aluminium.

In addition to these, there are many subsidiary groups of ternary and higher order alloys such as iron-cobalt-vanadium, nickel-iron-copper, iron-silicon-aluminium, nickel-copper-molybdenum-iron, etc., that have useful soft magnetic properties for special purposes. Usually the extra constituents are in the nature of additions that improve or facilitate the achievement of the intrinsic characteristics of the binary alloys, e.g. by increasing resistivity or saturation flux density, or by improving machinability or fabrication properties.

Commercially-available Magnetic Irons and Steels

Fig. 2–3 gives typical magnetization curves and compositions for five materials which represent practical approximations to pure unalloyed iron and are suitable for D.C. applications. In all cases the material has been annealed.

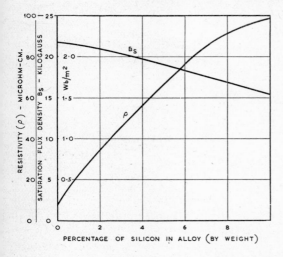

Fig. 2–5.—EFFECT OF
SILICON ON MAGNETIC
AND PHYSICAL PROPER-
TIES OF IRON.

Armco iron is manufactured in U.S.A. and material of this quality and purity is not readily available in this country at present. Low-carbon steels either cast or in rolled sections or sheets are generally used. Annealing subsequent to fabrication— particularly after cold working—is of great importance if the best magnetic properties are to be obtained from these materials. The effect of such heat-treatment on Armco iron previously strained by cold working is shown in Fig. 2–4.

Iron-silicon Alloys

Iron-silicon alloys were originated towards the end of the nineteenth century with the important researches carried out by Barrett, Brown and Hadfield.[6] Prior to this the bulk of the magnetic material used for electrical purposes was a so-called low-carbon-content steel. This material was generally used in the form of sheets, hot-rolled to thicknesses of 0·013–0·020 in. and it had a total loss of 2–4 W/lb. at 50 c/s and a flux density of 1 Wb/m² (10 kilogauss). It was found that the addition of 2–3 per cent. of silicon to iron which was in other respects considerably purer than had hitherto been used had the effect of reducing the total loss by a factor of two or three times. This improvement was due in part to the higher resistivity of the iron-silicon alloy as compared with low-carbon steel, so reducing the eddy-current losses under alternating magnetization. The improvement was also due to the greater purity of the basic materials used, which helped to increase the permeability and reduce the hysteresis losses, and to the chemical reactions of silicon with harmful impurities which virtually eliminated ageing.

A disadvantage for some purposes was the reduction in saturation density due to magnetic dilution as shown in Fig. 2–5 ; but with so many other advantages to their credit and despite their higher production cost, these improved alloys effectively superseded low-carbon steel for many electrical purposes. Even now they constitute by far the biggest proportion of magnetic materials in power-frequency plant.

Since these early investigations, much systematic research has been conducted into the factors affecting the magnetic quality of iron-silicon alloys. By controlled variation of the proportions of carbon, manganese, sulphur, phosphorous, nitrogen, oxygen and other impurities, and by purification of the basic iron as already described, a number of investigators (notably Yensen and Cioffi) have built up a fairly comprehensive picture of impurity effects on iron-silicon alloys. These data have been amassed on a laboratory or small-production scale. The superior qualities which they reveal for specific alloys and treatments cannot in general be attained economically in commercial production. For example, Goertz [7] has achieved a maximum permeability of 3,800,000 for a single crystal of 6·5 per cent. silicon-iron alloy when magnetized along a cube-edge after heat treatment in a magnetic field. Alloys with compositions in this region were known to have very low magnetostriction so that it was to be expected that very good magnetic softness would be measured on such a sample. However, materials with such a high percentage of silicon are practically impossible to handle on a commercial scale owing to their excessive brittleness and unworkability. Practical considerations of manufacture and fabrication limit the silicon content to $4\frac{1}{2}$ per cent. for hot-rolled materials in most practical cases, although in U.S.A. alloys with up to $5\frac{1}{2}$ per cent. of silicon have been used occasionally.

Use of Cold Reduction

The majority of iron-silicon materials are produced by hot rolling from ingots to sheet, but two newer processes are now in use which represent important advances in the techniques of manufacture. Both involve cold reduction of the material to give a final product in the form of continuous thin strip. The first method does not produce any marked improvement in magnetic properties as compared with hot-rolled sheet : but the strip has a better surface finish giving improved space factor when assembled as laminations ; its freedom from surface scale causes less wear on tools ; it is suitable for feeding continuous automatic presses ; and it allows of improved working conditions for personnel in the rolling mills.

Grain-orientation

The second method is of greater importance as regards magnetic properties. Cold-reduction processes on iron-silicon alloys produce a material having a grain-orientation that gives magnetic properties, in the direction of rolling of the strip, similar to those exhibited by single crystals when magnetized along a direction of easy magnetization.

The pronounced magnetic anisotropy of a single crystal of silicon-iron has been recorded by Williams [8] and is illustrated in Fig. 2-6. The crystal lattice is a body-centred cube and magnetization along a cube edge (the easy direction) can be carried out without domain rotation—the domains being already aligned in this direction or in directions at 90° or 180° to it. This gives magnetic properties outstandingly better than polycrystalline non-oriented hot-rolled silicon-iron.

In 1935 [9] Goss described a method of producing strip silicon-iron by which magnetic characteristics similar to those obtained for single crystals magnetized in the cube-edge direction could be achieved. It involved the production of hot-rolled strip followed by cold reduction of about 60 per cent., an intermediate anneal and subsequent cold reduction of a further 60 per cent. to final thickness followed by a final high-temperature anneal to induce re-crystallization and grain growth with preferred orientation. The method has been perfected by various workers as regards amounts of cold reduction and details of heat treatments, and the importance of controlled purity in obtaining a high degree of preferred orientation has been established.

The process has not so far been applied commercially to

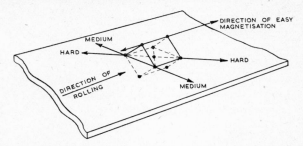

Fig. 2–6.—MAGNETIZATION DIRECTIONS IN GRAIN-ORIENTED IRON-SILICON ALLOY STRIP.

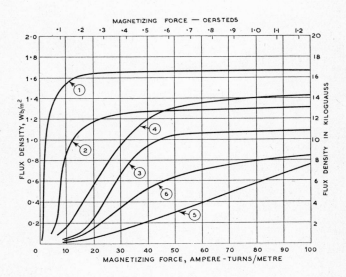

Fig. 2–7.—MAGNETIZATION CHARACTERISTICS OF VARIOUS IRON-SILICON ALLOY STRUCTURES.

Curve No.	Crystal Structure	Direction of Magnetization	Reduction Treatment	Per cent. Silicon
1	Single crystal	Cube edge	—	3·8
2	Single crystal	Face diagonal	—	3·8
3	Single crystal	Cube diagonal	—	3·8
4	Polycrystalline	Direction of rolling	Cold rolled	3·0
5	Polycrystalline	Across direction of rolling	Cold rolled	3·0
6	Polycrystalline	Direction of rolling	Hot rolled	4·0

materials containing more than about $3\frac{1}{2}$ per cent. of silicon because of the difficulty of working them cold.

The process results in grain orientation of the kind illustrated in Fig. 2–6. The plane of the rolled strip contains a direction of easy magnetization along a cube edge in the direction of rolling of the strip, i.e. along its length. A magnetization characteristic for such a material and magnetization is shown in Fig. 2–7, together with a characteristic when magnetized at right angles

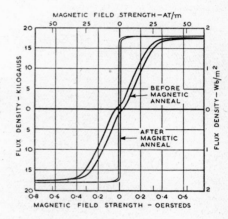

Fig. 2–8.—Hysteresis loops of a 6·5 per cent. silicon-iron single crystal before and after magnetic anneal (GOERTZ).

to the direction of rolling, i.e. across the strip or in the direction of the cube-face diagonals. This is a direction of less-easy magnetization and inferior properties result.

Magnetic Annealing

Two further recent lines of development that may lead to improvements in the quality of iron-silicon alloys can be mentioned. One has already been noted [7]—annealing in a magnetic field. This is most effective with silicon contents of the order of 6·4 per cent., and maximum permeabilities of about 200,000 are reported for pure polycrystalline specimens of such composition. The effect of magnetic annealing on the shape of the B–H loop for a 6·5 per cent. silicon single crystal is also noteworthy for its marked " rectangularity," Fig. 2–8.

Single-crystal Strip

The other development concerns the possibility of producing continuous strip which is in effect a single crystal. A laboratory method has been described by Dunn.[9, 10]

A strip of high purity and controlled composition, with a fine-grained polycrystalline structure to support grain growth, is used. A crystal of the preferred orientation is selected and isolated and crystal growth is propagated from this seed crystal by drawing the strip through a furnace in which there is an abrupt

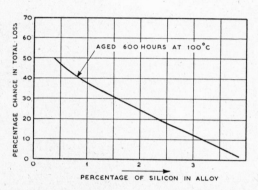

Fig. 2–9.—EFFECT OF SILICON ON MAGNETIC AGEING OF IRON-SILICON ALLOY, GIVING THE PERCENTAGE CHANGE IN TOTAL LOSS AT $B = 1\cdot3\,\text{Wb/m}^2$ (13,000 GAUSS) AFTER AGEING.

high-temperature gradient. The rate at which the strip passes through the gradient is made such that continuous crystal growth takes place. Crystals of any chosen orientation can be propagated by this method and it is therefore possible to have an orientation in which two easy directions of magnetization mutually at right angles lie in the plane of the strip. Maximum permeabilities of the order of 200,000 have been achieved in laminations cut with their legs parallel to the easy directions.

Investigations and results of such a kind may seem remote from the commercially-available materials now to be described. Nevertheless, it is on such researches that future progress depends ; they are invaluable in indicating the relative importance of the many factors affecting magnetic quality and in guiding magnetic material manufacturers towards more satisfactory products.

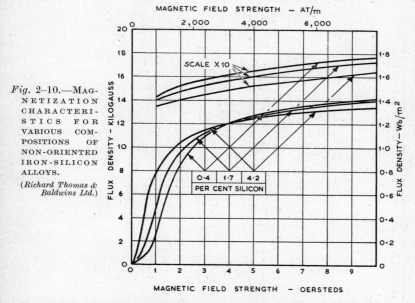

Fig. 2–10.—MAG-
NETIZATION
CHARACTERI-
STICS FOR
VARIOUS COM-
POSITIONS OF
NON-ORIENTED
IRON-SILICON
ALLOYS.

(*Richard Thomas &
Baldwins Ltd.*)

COMMERCIALLY-AVAILABLE IRON-SILICON ALLOYS

Hot-rolled Non-oriented Alloys

The importance of minimizing impurities has been discussed.
Scrap used for magnetic alloys is therefore selected to be as free
as possible from harmful ingredients. The raw materials are
usually melted and refined in an electric arc furnace and cast into
large ingots or slabs, which are soaked in pits at high temperature

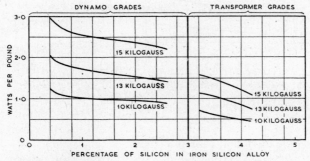

Fig. 2–11.—EFFECT OF SILICON ON TOTAL LOSSES OF NON-ORIENTED IRON-SILICON
ALLOYS.

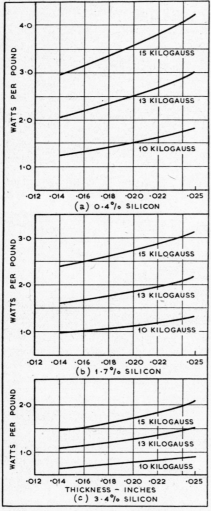

Fig. 2–12.—EFFECT OF THICKNESS ON TOTAL LOSSES OF NON-ORIENTED IRON-SILICON ALLOYS AT VARIOUS FLUX DENSITIES.

and subsequently passed through blooming mills and reduced to thick sheets. The sheets are folded and refolded with intermediate reheats and passes and hot-rolled as a pack of eight sheets to the final thickness of 0·014–0·030 in.; intermediate reheats may take place during pack rolling. Finally the pack is sheared, the sheets then separated and annealed in a controlled atmosphere to release strains and promote grain growth. As has already been mentioned, the best magnetic properties can only be achieved in a strain-free material and any subsequent mechanical strain induced in fabrication processes such as stamping or shearing should be relieved by further annealing in a protective atmosphere at 700°–800° C. followed by slow cooling.

Various grades and thicknesses of material are produced in bulk covering the range of percentages of silicon between 0·3 and $4\frac{1}{2}$ per cent. The intermediate grades are not widely used but are necessary to optimize specific apparatus design ; most of the material supplied is either in the region of 0·3–0·5 or 3·5–4 per cent. silicon. The reasons for this are discussed later in considering applications of the materials. Some typical characteristics for the range of com-

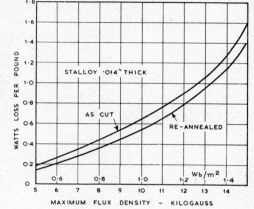

Fig. 2–13. — EFFECT OF ANNEALING AFTER CUTTING ON TRANSFORMER GRADE HOT-ROLLED IRON-SILICON ALLOY.

(*J. Sankey & Sons, Ltd.*)

mercially-available iron-silicon alloys are shown in Figs. 2–9 to 2–16.

Fig. 2–9 shows the beneficial effect on magnetic ageing of increasing silicon content. Ageing is seen to be virtually eliminated for transformer grades of sheet above 3 per cent. silicon.

Fig. 2–10 shows magnetization characteristics covering the range of commercially-available non-oriented alloys. The improved properties of the higher silicon alloys below about 1·2 Wb/m² (12 kilogauss) and the effect of magnetic dilution in reducing the saturation flux density are clearly visible.

Fig. 2–11 shows the variation in total loss with silicon content for both dynamo and transformer grades for three values of maximum flux density.

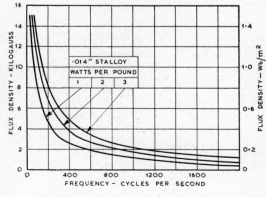

Fig. 2–14. — EFFECT OF FREQUENCY ON TOTAL LOSSES IN TRANSFORMER GRADE IRON-SILICON ALLOY.

(*J. Sankey & Sons, Ltd.*)

Fig. 2–12 gives the variation in total loss with thickness for three values of maximum flux density and relate respectively to 0·4, 1·7 and 3·4 per cent. silicon-content alloys.

Fig. 2–13 shows the improvement in properties resulting from annealing transformer-grade alloy after cutting.

All the properties except those in Fig. 2–10 relate to magnetization by a sine wave variation of flux at 50 c/s. For normal power frequency working the dynamo grades are normally used in sheets about 0·016 in. thick, while the transformer grades are usually 0·014 in. thick. Thinner material, down to 0·007 in., is made for higher frequency applications, but is difficult to produce and its properties are generally inferior to those of cold-reduced grain-oriented material or some of the nickel-iron alloys. Fig. 2–14 shows the effect of frequency and flux density on total losses in 0·014-in. thick transformer grade non-oriented iron-silicon alloy for three typical working values of total loss.

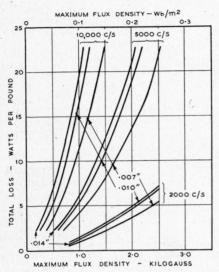

Fig. 2–15.—EFFECT OF LAMINATION THICK-
NESS ON LOSSES IN TRANSFORMER
GRADE IRON-SILICON ALLOY AT HIGH
FREQUENCIES.
(*Richard Thomas & Baldwins Ltd.*)

Fig. 2–15 shows the effect of lamination thickness on losses at three high frequencies. The 0·014-in. thick sample is of 3·9 per cent. silicon, while the 0·010 and 0·007-in. samples are of 3·6 per cent. silicon. In general, it is not possible to roll alloys of the highest silicon content to these small thicknesses, and the curves show that the properties of the 3·9 per cent., 0·014-in. samples are somewhat better than the 0·010-in. sample at 2,000 c/s. The effect of smaller thickness in reducing eddy current losses is shown to be very considerable at the higher frequencies.

Transformer-grade materials are frequently used with combined A.C. and D.C. excitations and Figs. 2–16 (a) and (b) show the effect of a polarizing field on incremental permeability for various

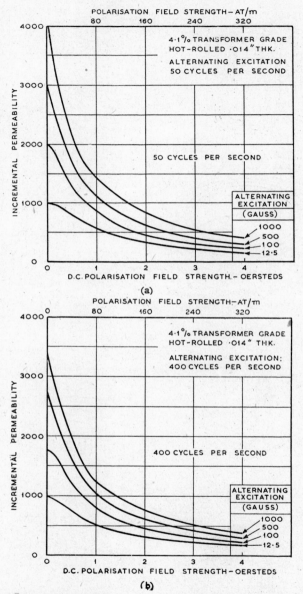

Fig. 2–16.—INCREMENTAL PERMEABILITY OF TRANSFORMER GRADE IRON-SILICON ALLOY AT 50 CYCLES PER SECOND AND 400 CYCLES PER SECOND.
(Richard Thomas & Baldwins Ltd).

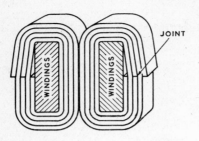

JOINT

Fig. 2–17 (*left*).—SECTION THROUGH TRANS-FORMER ASSEMBLY WITH PREFORMED WOUND AND CUT ORIENTED-STRIP CORE (BIRNSTINGL).
Strip size enlarged.

Fig. 2–18 (*below*).—PRECUT AND PRE-FORMED ORIENTED-STRIP CORE TRANS-FORMER ASSEMBLY.

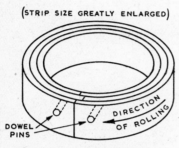

(STRIP SIZE GREATLY ENLARGED)

DOWEL PINS

DIRECTION OF ROLLING

PRECUT STRIP SUB-ASSEMBLY

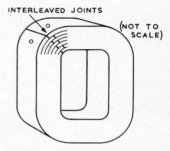

INTERLEAVED JOINTS

(NOT TO SCALE)

PREFORMED AND ANNEALED CORE SUB-UNIT

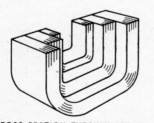

CROSS SECTION THROUGH CORE UNIT

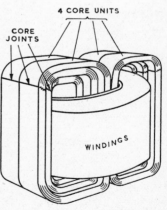

4 CORE UNITS

CORE JOINTS

WINDINGS

CORE AND COILS ASSEMBLY

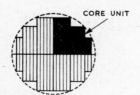

CORE UNIT

CROSS SECTION OF ASSEMBLY OF 4 CORE UNITS THROUGH CENTRE LEG

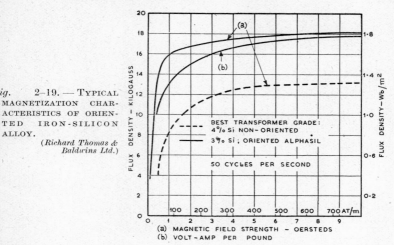

Fig. 2–19. — Typical Magnetization Characteristics of Oriented Iron-Silicon Alloy.
(*Richard Thomas & Baldwins Ltd.*)

BEST TRANSFORMER GRADE: 4% Si NON-ORIENTED

3% Si ; ORIENTED ALPHASIL

50 CYCLES PER SECOND

(a) MAGNETIC FIELD STRENGTH – OERSTEDS
(b) VOLT – AMP PER POUND

amplitudes of alternating excitations at 50 and 400 c/s respectively.

Cold-reduced, Non-oriented Alloys

These materials have magnetic characteristics similar to those described for the hot-rolled alloys ; they have the advantages already mentioned and do not require separate description. Some manufacturers reserve the right to supply hot- or cold-rolled material as alternatives.

Cold-reduced Oriented Alloys

Great progress has been made in America during the past decade in the commercial production of cold-reduced iron-silicon alloys, and more recently a material has been produced in this country of comparable quality. The materials contain between 3 and 3½ per cent. silicon and their production and properties have already been briefly described. To make best use of the superior characteristics it is necessary to magnetize them in the direction of rolling of the strip : magnetic circuits employing such materials have to be designed accordingly. The material is not normally applicable to rotating machinery, for directional properties are here a disadvantage. It has been used, however, in yokes for machines such as large turbo alternators. The laminations are arranged as narrow circumferential segments in which the

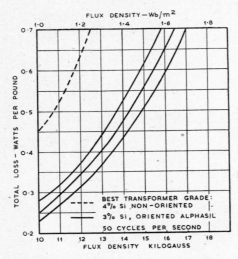

FLUX DENSITY — Wb/m²

TOTAL LOSS – WATTS PER POUND

FLUX DENSITY KILOGAUSS

BEST TRANSFORMER GRADE:
- - - - 4% Si NON-ORIENTED
——— 3% Si, ORIENTED ALPHASIL
50 CYCLES PER SECOND

Fig. 2–20.—TYPICAL TOTAL-LOSS CURVES FOR THREE GRADES OF ORIENTED IRON-SILICON ALLOY.

direction of rolling of the steel, and thus the direction of minimum loss, is arranged to be tangential to the bore of the stator. This permits either a reduction in the core loss occurring behind the stator teeth, or a reduction in the outside diameter of the machine with the same loss as would be obtained from hot-rolled non-oriented material. In large transformers and the like, cores are normally built up from plates or strips, the directional properties fit in conveniently with conventional manufacturing practice, and reduction in size and loss of about 30 per cent. as compared with non-oriented material is quite usual.

For smaller power transformers up to about 4,000 kVA new manufacturing techniques have been developed—principally in U.S.A.—to take advantage of the properties of oriented materials. Some of these techniques have been described by Birnstingl.[11] Two main methods are used. In one the core is preformed on a rectangular mandrel and annealed. After annealing the core retains its shape and the strip is cut through every other turn to give an interleaved joint pattern. The individual laminations are then threaded on to the coil assemblies where they readily take up their original preformed shape as shown in Fig. 2–17. This method is used for transformers up to about 600 kVA above which size threading of the laminations becomes difficult and may cause straining of the core material.

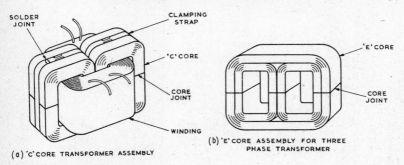

Fig. 2–21 (above).
—ORIENTED
STRIP CORE
CONSTRUCTIONS

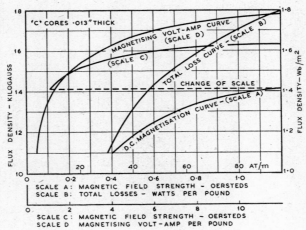

Fig. 2–22 (right).
—MAGNETIZA-
TION CHARAC-
TERISTICS FOR
" C " CORES OF
ORIENTED IRON-
SILICON ALLOY
STRIP 0·013 IN.
THICK.

(English Electric
Co., Ltd.)

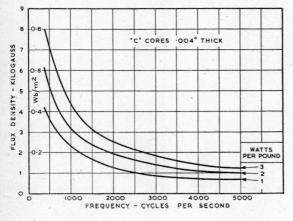

Fig. 2–23 (left).—
CURVES OF VARIA-
TION OF TOTAL LOSS
WITH FREQUENCY
AND FLUX DENSITY
FOR " C " CORES OF
ORIENTED IRON-
SILICON ALLOY
STRIP 0·004 IN.
THICK.

(English Electric Co., Ltd.)

E 2

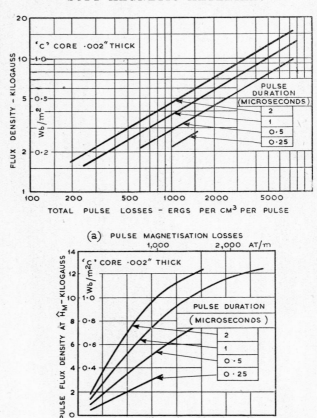

(a) PULSE MAGNETISATION LOSSES

(b) PULSE MAGNETISATION CHARACTERISTICS

Fig. 2-24.—PULSE MAGNETIZATION PROPERTIES OF "C" CORES OF ORIENTED
IRON-SILICON ALLOY STRIP 0·002 IN. THICK.

(*English Electric Co., Ltd.*)

The other method is used for large assemblies : steps in the process are illustrated in Fig. 2–18. The largest lamination is cut to length and bent into a circle, the position of the joint being located by dowel pins and holes. Further laminations are laid within the first, the lengths being progressively varied and the locating holes staggered to give interleaved joints when assembled on the locating pins. The complete build-up is then pressed on

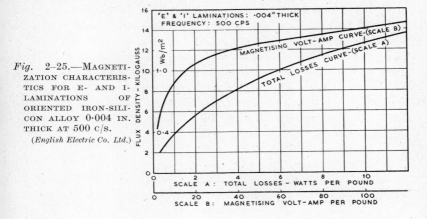

*Fig. 2–25.—*Magnetization characteristics for E- and I-laminations of oriented iron-silicon alloy 0·004 in. thick at 500 c/s.
(*English Electric Co. Ltd.*)

to a steel arbor and annealed *in situ.* Several strip widths may be used to approximate to a cylindrical central leg, and in larger units four such cores are assembled in a cylindrical winding. The making of preformed cores has been mechanized so that the complete process of core fabrication including insulating the laminations is carried out without handling.

Table 3, taken from Birnstingl's paper, compares the performance of three designs for a typical distribution transformer rating under conditions appropriate to the optimum working conditions for three methods of core construction. The advantages, both as regards weight and power saving, of the preformed design are apparent.

Table 3. Comparison of Transformer Performance for Various Forms of Iron-silicon Alloy Cores (Birnstingl)

Estimated performance figures for 1,000-kVA 33/0·44 kV 50-c/s distribution transformer

Type of core	Flux density		Magnetizing force		Iron loss Watts/lb.	Relative core Weights	Relative iron loss
	Kilolines/in.²	Wb/m²	AT/in. (R.M.S.)	AT/m (R.M.S.)			
Non-oriented sheet . .	85	1·3	5·5	220	1·0	100	100
Oriented sheet . .	90	1·4	2·5	100	0·8	93	75
Oriented preformed strip .	100	1·55	2·7	110	0·8	78	63

Fig. 2–19 shows typical A.C. magnetization and volt-ampere characteristics for the best quality of oriented strip at present commercially produced in Britain. For comparison, an A.C. magnetization characteristic for the best grade of 4 per cent. non-oriented silicon alloy is also shown. Fig. 2–20 shows typical total loss curves for similar oriented materials and also for the non-oriented alloy. The superior properties, both as regards losses and ability to operate at high flux density without undue magnetizing current, are apparent.

C-core Construction

For miniature transformers a range of cores has been developed which consist of two solidified C-shaped units. In one method these are made by winding continuous oriented strip on to a rectangular mandrel ; the core is annealed to relieve strains due to the winding process and solidified with a suitable impregnant. The solid core is then cut into two C-shaped pieces, the cut surfaces being ground and etched to ensure minimum air gap and to remove cutting burrs. The coil assembly is fitted between the halves of the core which are held together by a metal strap, as shown in Fig. 2–21 (a). A range of core assemblies suitable for use in three-phase components has recently been developed. The method of construction is indicated in Fig. 2–21 (b).

The presence of two airgaps in the magnetic circuit increases the magnetizing volt-amperes compared with corresponding uncut spiral cores, but the losses are unaffected and the C-core construction allows the superior properties of grain-oriented material to be utilized in a convenient manner, with conventional windings. Standardization and ease of assembly are important advantages of the construction.

Core assemblies of these kinds are produced by several manufacturers in Britain using strip from the U.S.A. (Hipersil) and British materials such as Crystalloy and Alphasil. Strip is available in three ranges of thickness : 0·012–0·014 in., 0·004–0·005 in. and 0·002 in. The material is also manufactured in U.S.A. down to 0·001 in. or less. For detailed information on the characteristics of C-cores made up from these materials, the reader is referred to the manufacturers' handbooks and pamphlets.[12] Some typical characteristics useful in application of the three thickness ranges are given in Figs. 2–22, 2–23 and 2–24.

In general, these oriented steels are unsuitable for the production of conventional stampings for miniature transformers because of their inferior properties across the direction of rolling. Nevertheless, the smallest sizes of C-cores are difficult to manufacture with consistent characteristics and it has been found advantageous to produce a small range of E- and I-laminations 0·004 in. thick for use with power supplies of higher frequencies. Typical characteristics for these laminations are shown in Fig. 2–25.

IRON-NICKEL ALLOYS

The iron-nickel group of alloys contains several of the most important soft-magnetic materials that are used for special applications. Compared with the iron-silicon alloys they are relatively expensive, but their special characteristics allow magnetic-component designers to achieve performances which would be impossible with orthodox materials. In general, they are of particular value in applications requiring very low losses in association with high permeabilities—both initial and maximum—but at comparatively low flux densities. Other alloys have constant permeability, rectangular hysteresis loops or other special properties.

Binary Alloys of Nickel and Iron

Although there had been earlier work on alloys of iron-nickel composition, the initial extensive researches on binary alloys of these elements were carried out by Yensen (1920) [13] and Elmen (1913–23).[14] These investigators explored the whole range of compositions and were responsible for segregating the magnetically-valuable regions ; in particular, Yensen did important work on compositions around 50 per cent. nickel which, as shown in Fig. 2–26, is a region of relatively high saturation flux density, while Elmen—latterly in association with Arnold—found and developed the high permeability region around 75–80 per cent. nickel and established the vital influence of correct heat treatment in optimizing magnetic properties. In this work they showed that by rapid and accurately-controlled quenching of these alloys after annealing, losses were reduced and initial permeability increased by factors of 3 or 4 over slowly cooled material. This treatment was called the Permalloy treatment and the alloys—Permalloys. The effect was most marked in the region 78·5 per cent. nickel, although a smaller maximum was also evident at about 45 per cent. nickel ; it is in these two regions that the majority of commercially available alloys lie although these are not always of pure binary composition.

High-resistivity Alloys

In addition to the two major groups of binary alloys just mentioned, there are other compositions with special properties. Fig. 2–26 shows a maximum in the resistivity curve at about 35 per cent. nickel and alloys have been developed to exploit this feature since the increased resistivity is advantageous in high frequency applications even although it is associated with lower permeability.

Temperature-sensitive Alloys

Alloys with about 30 per cent. nickel have a low Curie point of the order of 100° C., and consequently show a marked reduction in magnetization as temperature rises towards this value. Among other applications, this characteristic can be utilized for flux compensation in permanent and electro-magnet systems in which the field strength in the air gap tends to reduce with increasing temperature. A strip of this alloy shunting the gap diverts less flux as the temperature increases and can be arranged to maintain a constant flux in the air gap.

Grain-oriented Alloys

The development of a preferred grain-orientation in the direction of rolling of iron-silicon alloys has already been described, and it is interesting to note that a similar phenomenon had been reported by Smith, Garnett and Randall [15] for cold-rolled nickel-iron alloys as early as 1930. The effect is most pronounced in the region of 50 per cent. nickel, and processes have been developed by which strip of about this composition can be produced which has properties similar to those of a single crystal magnetized along an easy direction of magnetization. Preferred grain-orientation is achieved by ensuring high purity in the basic materials and by carefully controlled cold-reduction and heat treatment of the rolled strip. This results in grain-orientation of

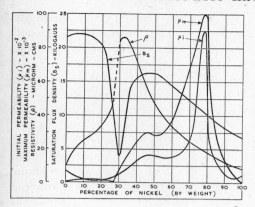

Fig. 2–26.—EFFECT OF COM-
POSITION ON MAGNETIC
AND ELECTRICAL PROPER-
TIES OF IRON-NICKEL
ALLOYS (ELMEN).

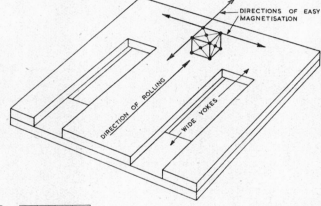

ig. 2–27.—MAG-
NETIZATION DI-
RECTIONS IN
RECTANGULAR
STAMPINGS (IN-
TERLEAVED)
MADE FROM
GRAIN - ORIENTED
50/50 IRON -
NICKEL ALLOY
STRIP.

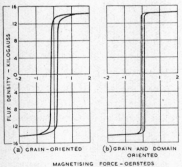

Fig. 2–28.—HYSTERESIS LOOPS FOR
GRAIN-ORIENTED AND GRAIN-
AND-DOMAIN-ORIENTED 50/50
IRON-NICKEL ALLOY.

(*Telegraph Construction & Maintenance Co. Ltd.*)

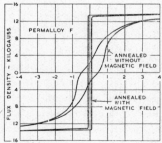

Fig. 2–29.—EFFECT OF HEAT
TREATMENT IN A MAGNETIC
FIELD ON THE HYSTERESIS
LOOP OF PERMALLOY F
(BOZORTH AND DILLINGER).

the kind shown in Fig. 2–27. It is seen that the grains have two directions of easy magnetization in the plane of the strip surface ; one in the direction of rolling, the other at right angles to it, i.e. across the strip.

Magnetization takes place by 90° or 180° domain re-orientations at low fields and losses associated with domain rotation at high fields are almost completely eliminated, resulting in a material of high permeability and low-hysteresis. loss with a rectangular hysteresis loop as shown in Fig. 2–28 (a). A material of this kind can clearly be used in the form of rectangular punchings since orthogonal directions of easy magnetization lie in the plane of the strip. To minimize the effects of airgaps the punchings have wide yokes and are interleaved as shown in Fig. 2–27.

Domain-oriented Alloys

It was found by Bozorth and Dillinger [16] that rectangular hysteresis loops could be produced in binary alloys with 60 to 80 per cent. nickel, if these were cooled from above the Curie temperature in the presence of a magnetic field. The rectangular loop characteristic was developed in the directions parallel and anti-parallel to the applied field and the effect was most pronounced in the region of high magnetostriction and high Curie temperature, i.e. about 65 per cent. nickel. Fig. 2–29 illustrates it for a material of this composition.

Grain- and domain-oriented Alloys

The properties of the grain-oriented materials may be improved still further by eliminating 90 per cent. domain re-orientations which require more energy than 180° reversals. This is done in a similar manner to that described for domain oriented materials by annealing grain-oriented strip in a magnetic field which is coaxial with the direction of rolling, and cooling in the presence of the field, through the Curie point temperature. This process leaves all the domains aligned in the easy direction nearest to the applied field. Magnetization processes then take place solely by 180° reversals. A very high degree of rectangularity and low coercive force and hysteresis loss result from this treatment as shown in Fig. 2–28 (b).

The same practical limitations arise in the use of these and the domain-oriented materials as were mentioned for grain-oriented

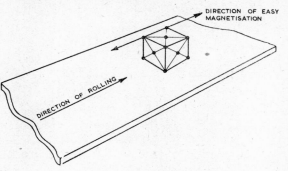

Fig.2–30.—MAGNETIZA-
TION DIRECTIONS IN
GRAIN- AND DOMAIN-
ORIENTED 50/50
IRON-NICKEL ALLOY
STRIP.

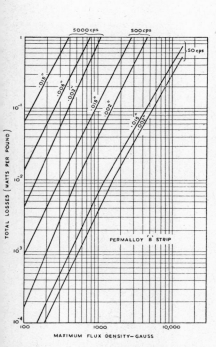

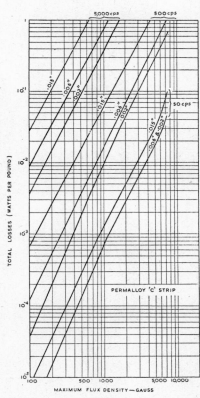

Fig. 2–31 (a).—VARIATION OF TOTAL
LOSSES WITH FLUX DENSITY IN
PERMALLOY " B " FOR VARIOUS FRE-
QUENCIES AND THICKNESSES.
(*Standard Telephones & Cables Ltd.*)

Fig. 2–31 (b).—VARIATION OF TOTAL
LOSSES WITH FLUX DENSITY IN
PERMALLOY " C " FOR VARIOUS FRE-
QUENCIES AND THICKNESSES.
(*Standard Telephones & Cables Ltd.*)

iron-silicon alloys. Since there is only one direction of easy magnetization as shown in Fig. 2–30, the best properties can be obtained only in the direction of rolling.

Ternary and Higher Order Alloys

There are relatively few commercially-available alloys of simple binary composition ; the majority of the materials which have compositions in the regions of the two important binary groups are manufactured with one or more additives—usually in minor proportions. The purpose of these is generally to decrease the sensitivity of the alloys to heat treatment so that the requirement for closely-controlled processes such as the Permalloy one described by Elmen is, to some extent, relaxed ; and also with certain compositions, to increase the resistivity while retaining or improving the desirable properties of the binary alloys. A disadvantage of the alloying process is that it is usually accompanied by a reduction in saturation density.

Various properties and characteristics of some commercially available materials in these groups are given later, and those of a few materials with special properties are described, below.

Supermalloy

The most commonly used additives are copper, chromium, molybdenum and manganese, and the highest permeability and lowest losses have been achieved by Boothby and Bozorth [17] (1947) with an alloy of composition 79 per cent. Ni, 15 per cent. Fe, 5 per cent. Mo and 0·5 per cent. Mn, known commercially as Supermalloy. When heat treated in pure hydrogen at 1,300° C. and cooled at a critical rate, initial permeabilities of over 100,000, maximum permeabilities of 1,500,000 and hysteresis losses of less than 0·1 J/m^3 (5 ergs/cm ^{3}) at 0·5 Wb/m^2 (5,000 gauss) have been reported ; saturation flux density for this material is about 0·8 Wb/m^2 (8,000 gauss), and resistivity 60 microhm-cm.

Constant Permeability Alloys

Two further groups of ternary alloys have useful applications ; both are concerned with achieving constant permeability and low hysteresis losses ; one at comparatively low values of flux densities and magnetic field strengths, the other at high values. The low-value alloys have been called Permivars and the high-value ones Isoperms.

Permivar

A typical Permivar alloy has a composition 45 per cent. Ni ; 30 per cent. Fe ; 25 per cent. Co, but materials with various composition are made giving a fairly wide range of properties. The material mentioned has a constant permeability of about 500 and negligible hysteresis loss, coercive force or remanence up to a maximum magnetic field strength of about 2 oersteds. Above this value hysteresis loss increases rapidly, the hysteresis loop having a constricted portion around the origin. The properties of very low coercive force and remanence are retained so that the loop is like a dumb-bell in contour. Near saturation, at higher fields, the hysteresis loop is of orthodox shape. A disadvantage of the material is that the constant permeability characteristic is destroyed if it is subjected to a high magnetizing force and can only be restored by being heat treated again.

Isoperm

This material is of German origin and again a wide range of compositions and properties exist. The alloys usually contain copper up to about 15 per cent. and nickel from 35–50 per cent., the remainder being iron. They have constant permeabilities of from 50–110 up to field strengths as high as 100 oersteds. A direction of easy magnetization at right angles to the plane of the rolled strip is induced by drastic cold reduction of about 98 per cent., followed by annealing and further cold reduction. This results in a texture which gives high permeability at right angles to the plane of the strip but low and constant permeability along it.

High Initial Permeability Alloy
" 1040 " Alloy

This alloy is characterized by very high initial permeability— about 40,000 and resistivity (56 microhm-cm). Its composition is 72 per cent. nickel, 14 per cent. copper, 3 per cent. molybdenum, the remainder being iron. Saturation flux density is low ($0 \cdot 62$ Wb/m^2 or 6,200 gauss) as also is hysteresis loss ($1 \cdot 5$ J/m^3 or 15 ergs/cm ^{3} per cycle).

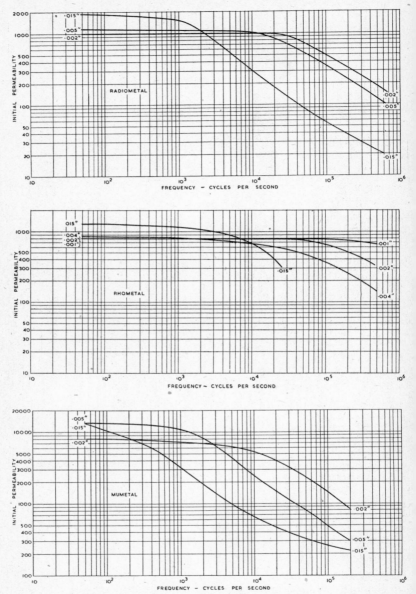

Fig. 2–32.—VARIATION OF INITIAL PERMEABILITY OF RADIO-, RHO- AND MUMETALS
WITH FREQUENCY FOR VARIOUS THICKNESSES.

(*Telegraph Construction & Maintenance Co. Ltd.*)

COMMERCIALLY-AVAILABLE IRON-NICKEL ALLOYS

Manufacture

It has already been mentioned that the majority of commercially-available alloys have various small metallic additions modifying the binary compositions. They are also subject to different heat and reduction schedules. For these reasons a detailed account of the preparation of the various alloys will not be given, but the following observations relate to manufacturing processes which are commonly in use.

The basic metals employed for the production of the alloys are specially selected to be free from harmful impurities such as carbon and sulphur, oxygen and nitrogen, either in free or combined states. Melting is usually carried out in a high-frequency induction furnace and in a controlled atmosphere ; for some alloys the process is carried out *in vacuo*, although this is expensive and only applied in special cases.

After melting the material is cast in ingots, which are machined to remove surface irregularities and impurities and subsequently rolled to sheet or strip. The first part of the rolling process is usually carried out under hot conditions, but the later stages of sheet or strip production involve extensive cold-rolling. This leaves the surface of the material in good condition and free from scale. At all stages in the process care is taken to ensure that the material is not exposed to contaminating atmospheres.

Laminations

Magnetic anisotropy is caused by the final cold-reduction process, the best properties being obtained in the direction of rolling. For this reason these materials are frequently used as " clockspring " toroids or " C " cores. However, they are also used in large quantities in the form of orthodox transformer punchings and other laminated structures. The useful range of thickness for laminations is from 0·015–0·004 in., but strip can be rolled down 0·001 in. or even 0·0005 in., although the magnetic properties are inferior for these small thicknesses. Toroids formed from thin strip are sometimes solidified with solventless resin to make them easier to handle.

Most iron-nickel alloys are sufficiently soft mechanically to be

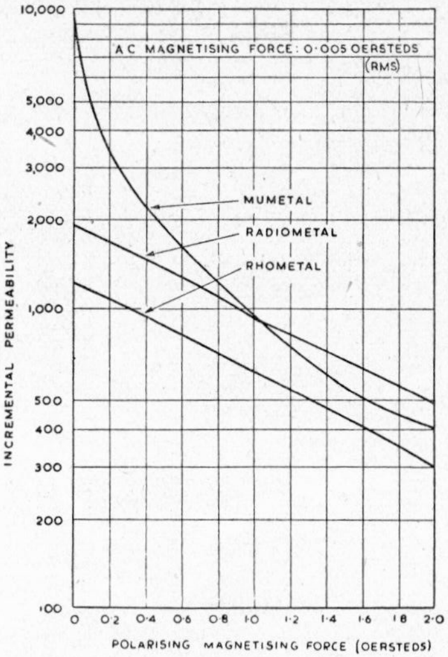

Table 4. Some Properties of Iron-Aluminium Alloys in comparison with Mumetal

Material	Permeability Initial	Permeability Maximum	Saturation Induction (gauss)	Hysteresis Loss (B = 5000 gauss) (ergs per cc per cycle)	Resistivity (microhm-cm)	Density (gm/cm³)
Mumetal	20,000 to 30,000	110,000	7800	38·5	60	8·8
Alperm	3000	55,000	8000	41*	140	6·5
16-Alfenol	4000	75,000 110,000	8000	76·4	153	6·5

* at B = 3000 gauss

Table 5. Comparison between Losses in Iron-Aluminium and Iron-Silicon Alloys

Material	Thickness	Losses in Watts per Pound at B max = 5000 gauss			
		60 cps	400 cps	1000 cps	2000 cps
16-Alfenol	·007"	0·05	0·7	2·7	8·6
16-Alfenol	·014"	0·045	0·95	5·2	12·0
Grain-oriented Iron Silicon Strip	·001"	—	1·2	3·2	7·5

Fig. 2-33.—VARIATION OF INCRE-
MENTAL PERMEABILITY OF RADIO-
METAL, RHOMETAL AND MUMETAL
WITH POLARIZING MAGNETIZING
FORCE.

(Telegraph Construction & Maintenance Co. Ltd.)

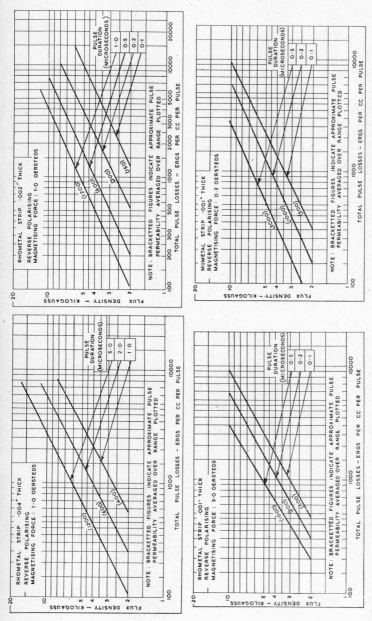

Fig. 2·34.—PULSE MAGNETIZATION PROPERTIES OF RHOMETAL AND MUMETAL SHOWING VARIATION OF TOTAL LOSSES WITH FLUX DENSITY FOR VARIOUS PULSE DURATIONS AND THICKNESSES WITH SUPERIMPOSED REVERSE POLARIZING MAGNETIZATION (MELVILLE [24]).

M.A.F

F

fabricated into stampings, etc., in the cold-rolled state, but to develop the best magnetic properties, the final heat treatment at high temperature and in a protective or reducing atmosphere is carried out after all working processes have been completed. The magnetic properties of these alloys are relatively sensitive to mechanical strains, and any deformation after final annealing is to be avoided.

Insulating the Laminations

In A.C. applications it is necessary to provide insulation between the laminæ in stacked assemblies so as to avoid excessive eddy currents. Three methods are in common use. For low-frequency applications where very high resistivity in the inter-laminar film is not essential, a thin layer of oxide is allowed to form on the surface of the material by exposing it to the air after the high-temperature annealing process while it is still sufficiently hot for oxidation to take place.

For higher frequencies, one side of the strip or lamination is covered with a thin layer of lacquer. This results in a good homogenous film of high resistivity but yields a lower stacking factor, particularly with very thin materials.

The method just described is not suitable for applications in which the final high-temperature anneal must take place after assembly. In these cases a layer of refractory material, such as magnesium oxide in fine suspension, is deposited on the surface of the strip while it is being wound to its final configuration and the complete assembly is heat-treated, the insulating properties of the refractory material being unaffected by high temperature or the protective or reducing atmosphere.

Non-laminated Parts

In D.C. magnetic circuits it is sometimes convenient to use machined parts or small forgings of high-permeability alloy. Some of the materials can be produced in these forms or as various rolled or drawn sections or pressings. High-temperature annealing is necessary after these processes to develop the best magnetic properties, and an upper limit to the size of sections which may be usefully dealt with is determined by the inferior properties which result due to non-uniform heat · treatment through large sections.

Magnetic Properties

Table 2, p. 39, gives some relevant data for several alloys covering the principal categories of special magnetic characteristics.

Figs. 2–31 to 2–34 show various properties and characteristics chosen to illustrate the conditions of magnetization for which the several alloys are best suited.

IRON-COBALT ALLOYS

Alloys in this group are of interest primarily because of their high magnetic saturation induction and their relatively high permeability at high field strengths. In comparison with other soft magnetic materials they are very expensive owing to the high cost of cobalt, but for some purposes their special properties are of great value.

The binary alloys were investigated and the useful properties of alloys with 35–50 per cent. cobalt were appreciated by Weiss as long ago as 1913.[18] Nevertheless, in addition to their high cost, the simple alloys have the major drawback that they are almost impossible to fabricate either hot or cold, so that despite having the highest saturation induction of any magnetic material (about 2·5 Wb/m^2 or 25,000 gauss), little practical use could be made of them. In 1932 White and Wahl patented a range of ternary alloys in which a few per cent. of vanadium was added to equal quantities of cobalt and iron and the alloys rendered workable by hot rolling and quenching. Magnetic properties were adversely affected by the addition of the third element, but a compromise between magnetic quality and workability has been achieved at about 2 per cent. vanadium when the saturation induction is about 23,000 gauss with the advantage of increased resistivity.

More recently (1947) a similar alloy was reported by Stanley and Yensen [20] in which the ternary element is about $\frac{1}{2}$ per cent. of chromium. Only 35 per cent. of cobalt is used in this alloy, which is therefore somewhat less expensive on basic materials ; in other respects its properties are similar to the Vanadium alloy but with a slightly higher saturation induction at very high field strengths.

Fig. 2–35 shows a comparison between the magnetization

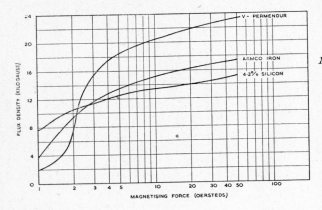

Fig. 2–35.—Com-
parison of
magnetization
characteristics
for v-per-
mendur, armco
iron and 4·2 per
cent. iron-
silicon alloy.

Fig. 2–36.—Variation
of total losses
with thickness in
v-permendur for
various flux den-
sities and fre-
quencies.
(Standard Telephones &
Cables Ltd.)

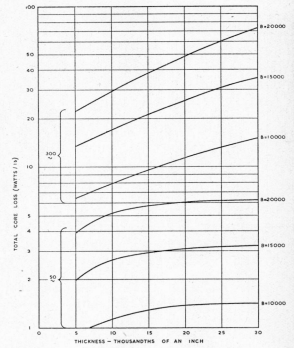

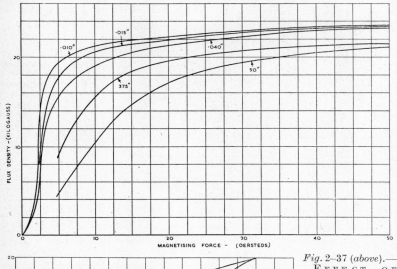

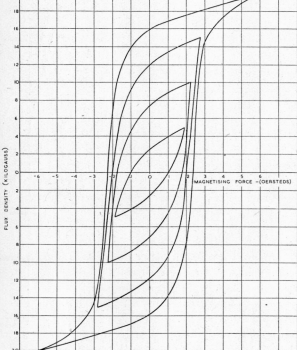

Fig. 2–37 (above).—
EFFECT OF
THICKNESS ON
MAGNETIZATION
CURVES OF V-
PERMENDUR.

Fig. 2–38 (left).—
TYPICAL FAMILY
OF HYSTERESIS
LOOPS FOR V-
PERMENDUR
(0·010 IN. STRIP).

curves for V-Permendur (the commercial name for the vanadium alloy), Armco iron and 4·2 per cent. silicon-iron. The superiority of the iron-cobalt alloy at high inductions is immediately apparent. Figs 2–36 to 2–38 give some relevant data for V-Permendur, which is commercially available in this country.

IRON-ALUMINIUM ALLOYS

Alloys in this group have achieved little commercial application, but deserve mention because of their desirable magnetic properties. Preliminary investigations into their magnetic possibilities were carried out by Barrett, Brown and Hadfield at about the same time as their work, already mentioned, on iron-silicon alloys. The aluminium alloys showed two major practical disadvantages. Aluminium was at that time comparatively expensive and the formation of a very hard oxide skin on the surface of slabs during hot-rolling made fabrication an extremely difficult and costly process. For these reasons they did not find favour.

On the credit side the aluminium alloys were found to have magnetic properties which as regards losses, saturation density, resistivity, inhibiting of ageing, etc., were in every way comparable with the corresponding silicon alloys ; also they were not subject to the embrittling effect experienced with increased silicon content.

Since these early investigations several workers have re-examined the alloys from various aspects and a continual improvement in properties has been noticeable. In 1940 Bozorth, Williams and Morris reported [21] that by cold reduction and high temperature annealing of alloys with low aluminium content—of the order of $3\frac{1}{2}$ per cent.—properties similar to those of grain-oriented silicon-iron could be produced. These had the additional important advantage however that two directions of easy magnetization at right angles to each other lie in the plane of the rolled sheet—one being in the direction of rolling.

During and since World War II there has been a revival of interest in the alloys as substitutes for iron-nickel alloys since they do not require strategically valuable or scarce materials. The effect of heat treatment on various compositions up to 17 per cent. aluminium was investigated in Japan by Masumoto and Saito [22] and a material with about 16 per cent. aluminium known as Alperm was developed. This has properties similar to Mumetal. A detailed study of fabrication methods for a similar material—16-Alfenol—has been described by Nachman and Buchler.[23] The preferred process which they have evolved is briefly as follows.

Manufacture

Electrolytically-pure iron and aluminium are melted *in vacuo* and the material chill-cast into slabs about 1 in. thick and 10 lb. weight, the moulds being specially lined. The slabs are trimmed and hot rolled at 1,000° C., being reduced about 0·005 in. per pass and reheated initially after each four passes and latterly after each two passes until the thickness has been reduced to about $\frac{1}{8}$ in. This thick strip is then reduced to thin strip 0·014 in. or 0·007 in. thick by " cold " reduction at 575° C. If very thin strip is required the thin strip is annealed for 24 hours at 575° C. and further cold reduction carried out at room temperature after the hard oxide skin formed during previous treatment has been removed electrolytically. By these methods strip as thin as 0·0003 in. has been produced. The finished strip is annealed at 1,000° C. for about two hours in pure dry hydrogen and cooled in the furnace to 600° C. from which temperature it is quenched in water.

Properties

This process results in a material of high resistivity and low anisotropy with D.C. properties which, with the exception of initial permeability, are comparable with those of Mumetal, Table 4, p. 72. Its high resistivity makes it attractive for A.C. applications, and from Table 5 it is seen that even at 2,000 c/s and 0·5 Wb/m² (5 kilogauss) the losses in 0·007 in. and 0·014 in. laminations compare favourably with 0·001 in. silicon-iron strip. Also the ability to produce very thin strip may be important in reducing losses at even higher frequencies. Interlaminar insulation of good quality is formed automatically during fabrication.

It is difficult to predict what the future of such a material might be. The fabrication process as outlined above is clearly an expensive one and economic progress probably depends on the extent to which it can be simplified.

APPLICATIONS OF SOFT MAGNETIC MATERIALS

This summary of the uses to which soft magnetic materials may be put is not intended to be comprehensive but rather to assist magnetic component designers to choose the magnetic materials with the properties most appropriate to their applications. Only those materials which have been described in the foregoing text will be dealt with.

Soft Irons and Steels

These materials, which include electrolytic iron, Armco iron, Swedish charcoal iron and low-carbon steel, are characterized by low resistivity and high permeability at high flux densities. They are therefore most suited to D.C. applications in which high flux densities are required with small magnetizing forces. Typical magnetization characteristics are given in Fig. 2–3.

Applications include relay yokes, armatures and cores, electro-magnet yokes and pole pieces, A.C.- and D.C.-machine frames and pole pieces, A.C.-generator rotors and a wide variety of special equipment such as electromagnetic chucks, clutches and the like. The materials are produced in various forms to suit the applications ; for example, motor frames are cast in low-carbon steel or fabricated from rolled plate and the cores of large electro-magnetic structures are frequently forged ; small components are usually assembled from stamped, pressed or drawn parts of thick sheet. In general, the materials require to be annealed after working to develop the best magnetic properties.

Applications of Iron-Silicon Alloys

These alloys may be considered in three groups : low- and high-silicon content and grain-oriented materials. Low-silicon alloys—up to say $2\frac{1}{2}$ per cent. silicon—are usually called dynamo grades, and are widely used in ordinary motor and generator construction. Material with less than about $\frac{1}{2}$ per cent. silicon is used for cheaper grades of small motors for intermittent duty, and in parts of magnetic circuits in which high permeability at high flux density is of greater importance than low losses. From $1-2\frac{1}{2}$ per cent. silicon alloys are used for motors and generators of average efficiency, cheaper grades of small transformers and reactors and other application in which low cost is more important than high efficiency. From $2\frac{1}{2}$–3 per cent. silicon alloys are applied to motors and generators in which high efficiency is the over-riding consideration. They are also used for small- and medium-sized transformers which are not continuously rated but which do not merit the use of more costly high-quality grades.

The high-silicon alloys—from 3–$4\frac{1}{2}$ per cent.—are the normal materials for power and distribution transformers at power frequencies and for some parts of the associated alternators and other continuous-running machines and equipment in which low losses and high efficiency are of paramount importance. For economical construction, low losses must be associated with high working-flux densities and these materials represent the best compromise between these factors and a magnetic material which is not too costly to produce. On account of their high resistivity the high-silicon alloys are also suitable for use at audio frequencies for small-power and matching transformers.

The applications of grain-oriented iron-silicon alloy have already been described in some detail. The thicker strips are suitable for the highest efficiency transformers of all kinds operating at high flux densities and power frequencies, and are also used in some parts of associated rotating machinery. Made-up cores of thinner strip either as continuous " clocksprings " or C-cores are applied to a wide variety of purposes, particularly in the fields of electronics and telecommunications in which they are used for audio-frequency power transformers, chokes, pulse transformers, etc., in which low losses are important. They are also useful in magnetic amplifier and saturable reactor work in which their low losses and comparatively rectangular hysteresis loops are advantageous.

Applications of Iron-Nickel Alloys

The range of applications of these alloys is too great to catalogue in detail. There are four broad classifications other than the special materials such as those with constant permeability and high-temperature coefficient of induction already mentioned.

High Initial-permeability Alloys

This group includes Permalloy C and Mumetal. Their special characteristics are extremely low losses and high permeabilities at low flux densities, which features are of particular value in many electrical engineering and telecommunications applications. They are used in wide-band, instrument and other special transformers, in filter coils, as loading in submarine cables, as saturable reactor cores, for magnetic shielding, and in a wide variety of special components, such as sensitive high-speed relays, gramophone pick-ups and instrument armatures.

High Saturation-density Alloys

These alloys include Permalloy B and Radiometal. They are similar in properties to the best quality grain-oriented silicon-iron with somewhat lower saturation density. They are used in small power transformers at audio frequencies and for cores in transformers, chokes, relays, etc., with combined A.C. and D.C. magnetization, having comparatively high incremental permeability under these conditions.

High-resistivity Alloys

This group includes Permalloy D and Rhometal. These alloys are of value where eddy-current losses have to be minimized at very high rates of change of flux ; for very thin strip the change in initial permeability is small over a wide frequency band up to several hundreds of kilocycles. These characteristics are used in high-frequency generators, pulse transformers and high-frequency inductors and transformers.

Rectangular-loop Alloys

This group includes Permalloy F and H.C.R. metal. The special features of these alloys are high-saturation flux density and remanence, and low losses, coercivity and magnetizing current up to saturation which occurs at high flux density for a small proportional change in flux density. They are particularly useful in circuits in which an " inductive switching " action or "two-state " characteristic is required. Applications of this kind arise in mechanical-contact rectifiers, magnetic-pulse generators, magnetic amplifiers and magnetic memory-storage devices. They are also useful for components such as current transformers where low waveform distortion is required over a large change in flux density.

Construction of Laminated Assemblies of Iron-Nickel Alloys

It has already been mentioned that the best magnetic properties are obtained in these alloys in the direction of rolling of the strip. It is therefore advantageous, wherever possible, to use the material in the form of continuous-wound strip cores. This has economic as well as technical advantages over the use of stampings since there is no waste and no tool costs for punching tools ; also, assembly is simplified—particularly where very thin material is required. A disadvantage is that the windings have to be threaded through the core, but with modern winding techniques this is not a serious problem. In some cases C-core constructions are possible.

Applications of Iron-Cobalt Alloys

The commercially useful alloy is V-Permendur and is characterized by high permeability at very high flux densities. It is expensive and is used in those parts of magnetic circuits in which high flux densities for low magnetizing forces are required. When used for pole pieces of D.C. electro-magnet structures, parts may be rolled, forged or cast and machined. This material can also be supplied as thin sheets such as are used in telephone diaphragms, and is useful in A.C. circuits in this form. The best magnetic properties are attained when the material is thoroughly annealed after working.

Acknowledgments

The author is grateful to Messrs. Armco Ltd., English Electric Co. Ltd., Richard Thomas & Baldwins Ltd., J. Sankey & Sons Ltd., Standard Telephones & Cables Ltd., Telegraph Construction & Maintenance Co. Ltd., and the Steel Company of Wales for information about their products which they have generously given and permitted to be published, and to the authors and publishers of the various papers and articles given in the references on which he has drawn freely. He also wishes to thank the Directors of the British Thomson-Houston Co. Ltd. for permission to publish this chapter.

References

1. CIOFFI, P. P. " New High Permeabilities in Hydrogen-treated Iron," *Phys. Rev.*, 1934, **42**.
2. BOZORTH, R. M. " Directional Ferromagnetic Properties of Metals," *J. App. Phys.*, 1937, **8**.

3. YENSEN, T. D.   " Magnetic Properties of Ternary Fe-Si-C Alloys,"
   Trans. A.I.E.E., 1924, **43.**
4. YENSEN, T. D., and ZIEGLER, N. A.   " Effect of C, O and Grain Size on
   Magnetic Properties of Si-Fe." *Trans. Amer. Soc. Metals*, 1936, **24.**
5. ELMEN, G. W.   " Magnetic Alloys of Iron, Nickel and Cobalt," *J.
   Franklin Inst.*, 1929, **207.**
6. BARRETT, W. F., BROWN, W., and HADFIELD, R. A.   " Electrical
   Conductivity and Magnetic Permeability of Various Alloys of Iron,"
   Sci. Trans. Roy. Dublin Soc., 1900, **7** ; *J.I.E.E.*, 1902, **31.**
7. GOERTZ, M.   " Iron Silicon Alloys Heat-treated in a Magnetic Field,"
   J. App. Phys., 1951, **22.**
8. WILLIAMS, H. J.   " Magnetic Properties of Single Crystals of Silicon
   Iron," *Phys. Rev.*, 1937, **52.**
9. GOSS, N. P.   " New Developments in Electrolytic Strip Steels Characterized by Fine Grain Structure Approaching Properties of a
   Single Crystal." *Trans. Amer. Soc. Metals*, 1935, **23.**
10. DUNN, C. G.   " Controlled Grain Growth Applied to the Problem of
    Grain Boundary Energy Measurements," *Journ. of Metals Trans.*,
    Jan., 1949.
11. BIRNSTINGL, D. W.   " Some Recent Advances in American Trans-
    former Manufacture," *J.I.E.E.*, March, 1954.
12. " A Handbook for Designers of Transformers for the Electronic
    Industry " issued by English Electric Co. Ltd.
    Pamphlets issued by Telcon-Magnetic Cores Ltd. and J. Sankey &
    Sons Ltd.
13. YENSEN, T. D.   " Magnetic and Electrical Properties of Iron, Nickel
    and Cobalt," *Journ. A.I.E.E.*, 1920, **39.**
14. ELMEN, G. W., and ARNOLD, H. D.   " Permalloy—An Alloy of Remark-
    able Magnetic Properties," *J. Franklin Inst.*, 1923, **195.**
15. SMITH, W. S., GARNETT, H. J., and RANDALL, W. F.   Brit. Pat.
    366,523—1930.
16. DILLINGER, J. F., and BOZORTH, R. M.   " Heat Treatment of Magnetic
    Materials in a Magnetic Field.   Survey of Iron-Cobalt-Nickel Alloys,"
    Physics, 1935, **6.**
17. BOOTHBY, O. L., and BOZORTH, R. M.   " A New Magnetic Material of
    High Permeability," *J. App. Phys.*, 1947, **18.**
18. WEISS, P.   " Sur les champs magnetiques obtenus avec un electro-
    aimant muni de pieces polaires in ferro cobalt," *Comptes Rendus*,
    1913, **156.**
19. WHITE, J. H., and WAHL, C. V.   U.S. Patent 1,862,559—1932.
20. STANLEY, J. K., and YENSEN, T. D.   " Hiperco—A Magnetic Alloy,"
    Elec. Engrg., 1947, **66.**
21. BOZORTH, WILLIAMS and MORRIS.   " Magnetic Properties of Fe-Al
    Alloys," *Phys. Rev.*, 1940, **58.**
22. MAZUMOTO and SAITO.   " On the Effect of Heat Treatment on the
    Magnetic Properties of Iron-Aluminium Alloys," *Research Report
    Tohokw Univ.*, Japan, 1952.
23. NACHMAN and BUCHLER.   " The Fabrication and Properties of 16-
    Alfenol—a Non-strategic Aluminium-Iron Alloy," *Navord Report
    2819*, 1953.
24. MELVILLE, W. S.   " Pulse Magnetization of Nickel Irons from 0·1 to 5
    Microseconds," *J. I.E.E.*, 1950, Part 2, **97.**

2. (b) MAGNETICALLY-SOFT FERRITES

THE present section is devoted to a consideration of magneti-cally-soft ferrites which have a low coercivity combined with high permeability. The development of these materials was occasioned by the need for magnetic materials which could be used as the cores of high-frequency coils, chiefly in connection with radio and allied equipment. These ferro-magnetic oxides are known, in Britain, under the name of Ferroxcube.

The ferro-magnetic oxides are of such high specific resistance that the eddy-current losses are reduced to negligible proportions. The losses which occur in them are due to hysteresis and ferro-magnetic resonance absorption (i.e. residual losses).

ELECTRICAL AND MAGNETIC PROPERTIES

Ferroxcube, as far as its chemical composition is concerned, consists of mixed crystals of simple cubic ferrites with typical compositions MFe_2O_4, where M represents a divalent metal (a divalent metal can, in this instance, be either Cu, Mg, Mn, Ni, Fe or Zn) and crystallizing with the typical spinel structure $MgAl_2O_4$.

The material is characterized by high initial permeability μ_0, small coercivity H_c, and of such high resistivity that the need for laminating or powder-bonding the core, in order to reduce eddy current losses to reasonable limits, is obviated. The material is produced by processes similar to those used in the production of the common insulating ceramics and possesses comparable mechanical properties.

Ferroxcube is a homogeneous material—not a bonded powdered core—and therefore contains no internal air gaps. In certain circumstances it may be advantageous deliberately to introduce an air gap into the magnetic circuit, say in order to reduce the influence of temperature changes or harmonic distortion, or when the core is subjected to D.C. polarization superimposed upon the alternating induction. Air gaps are also used in Ferroxcube cores to obtain coils with the maximum " Q " factors over a given frequency range. The electrical and magnetic losses can be matched by the introduction of the appropriate air gap, a feature which is not always possible with powdered dust cores since in these there is always a fixed internal air gap.

Ferroxcube is now widely used in a variety of applications considerably greater than was originally envisaged. Such applications are in high quality coils, in carrier telephony, wide-band transformers, high-frequency power transformers, inter-mediate frequency transformers and deflection coils in television receivers, pulse transformers and the like.

There are two main types of Ferroxcube, both of which are ferrites having a cubic crystal structure. These types are :

    (1) Ferroxcube A—a range of manganese-zinc ferrites.

    (2) Ferroxcube B—a range of nickel-zinc ferrites.

Four grades of manganese-zinc ferrites have now been developed and five grades of nickel-zinc ferrites. In order to distinguish between each grade a colour code is used.

Ferroxcube B, of which there are five grades, differs consider-ably from Ferroxcube A, having in general lower values of initial permeability and saturation flux density, increased coercivity and Curie temperatures, and very high values of resistivity resulting in improved high frequency characteristics. A frequency range of from approximately 500 kc/s to 200 Mc/s is covered by the five grades. These materials show magnetostrictive properties. This makes them suitable for electro-mechanical filters and receiving transducers.

The tables show the electrical and magnetic properties of all grades of Ferroxcube. It should be emphasized that the figures quoted are nominal, the measurements being taken, for the greater part, on pressed ring specimens.

For extrusions in rod or tube form, somewhat inferior properties are obtained since it is difficult to obtain a density equal to that of a pressed piece part. In practice this does not represent a serious disadvantage as rods and tubes are usually in the " open circuit " condition where they will be working with severe " dilution " which is determined, for a given material, mainly by the dimensions of the core.

Permeability

It is found that the initial permeability of Ferroxcube materials increases as the flux density increases, up to a certain strength and thereafter decreases as the saturation point is approached. The point at which maximum permeability is reached depends upon the temperature.

ELECTRICAL AND MAGNETIC PROPERTIES OF FERROXCUBE TYPE A

(These are nominal figures and refer to conditions at 20° C. unless otherwise stated)

Ferroxcube grade	A1	A2	A3	A4
Frequency range (approx.) tuned applications . .		1 kc/s–500 kc/s.		
Frequency range (approx.) non-tuned applications . .		1 kc/s–20 Mc/s.		
Initial permeability (at induction $\geqslant$ 0·00075 Wb/m² or 7·5 gauss) . .	850		1,200	1,500
Loss factor $\dfrac{\tan \delta}{\mu_r}$ at 60 kc/s .	6×10^{-6}		10×10^{-6}	9×10^{-6}
,, ,, 250 ,, .	20×10^{-6}		27×10^{-6}	25×10^{-6}
,, ,, 450 ,, .	40×10^{-6}		57×10^{-6}	70×10^{-6}
Temp. factor of $\dfrac{1}{\mu_r^2}\dfrac{d\mu_r}{dT}$ per 0° C. (between 20° C. and 50° C.).	7×10^{-6}	4×10^{-6}	4×10^{-6}	4×10^{-6}
B_{sat} (H = 795 AT/m or 10 oersteds) at 20° C. (Wb/m²)	0·34	0·35	0·4	0·365
(gauss) .	3,400	3,500	4,000	3,650
,, ,, 100° C. ,, (Wb/m²) .	0·23	0·245	0·3	0·224
(gauss) .	2,300	2,450	3,000	2,240
H_c (AT/m) . .	31·8	31·8	31·8	23·85
(oersteds) .	0·4	0·4	0·4	0·3
Resistivity (ohm cm) . .	100	50	50	50
Curie point (° C.) . .	180	170	190	155
Specific gravity . . .	4·8	4·8	4·8	4·8

ELECTRICAL AND MAGNETIC PROPERTIES OF FERROXCUBE TYPE B

FERROXCUBE GRADE	B1	B2	B3	B4	B5
Frequency range (approx.) for tuned applications	1–500 kc/s	0·5–2 Mc/s	2–5 Mc/s	5–10 Mc/s	10–50 Mc/s
Frequency range (approx.) for non-tuned applications	1 kc/s–20 Mc/s	1–50 Mc/s	1–70 Mc/s	1–100 Mc/s	1–200 Mc/s
Initial permeability (at induction $\leqslant$ 0·00075 Wb/m² or 7·5 gauss)	650	200	125	57	20
Loss factor $\dfrac{\tan \delta}{\mu_r}$ at 60 kc/s	22×10^{-6}				
,, ,, ,, 250 ,,	38×10^{-6}				
,, ,, ,, 450 ,,	53×10^{-6}				
,, ,, ,, 0·5 Mc/s		90×10^{-6}			
,, ,, ,, 1 ,,		100×10^{-6}	95×10^{-6}		
,, ,, ,, 5 ,,			150×10^{-6}	170×10^{-6}	
,, ,, ,, 10 ,,				200×10^{-6}	350×10^{-6}
,, ,, ,, 20 ,,					380×10^{-6}
,, ,, ,, 30 ,,					700×10^{-6}
,, ,, ,, 40 ,,					$1{,}700 \times 10^{-6}$
,, ,, ,, 50 ,,					$2{,}500 \times 10^{-6}$
Temp. factor of μ_0, $\dfrac{1}{\mu_r^2} \cdot \dfrac{d\mu_r}{dT}$ per °C. (Between 20° C. and 50° C.)	8×10^{-6}	14×10^{-6}	15×10^{-6}	20×10^{-6}	30×10^{-6}
Magnetizing force H (AT/m)	795	1,590	2,385	4,770	6,360
(oersteds)	10	20	30	60	80
B_{sat} at 20° C. (Wb/m²)	0·29	0·32	0·27	0·25	0·19
(gauss)	2,900	3,200	2,700	2,500	1,900
B_{sat} at 100° C. (Wb/m²)	0·18	0·265	0·245	0·23	0·175
(gauss)	1,800	2,650	2,450	2,300	1,750
H_c (AT/m)	31·8	55-65	35-75	477	1,750
(oersteds)	0·4	1·7	4·5	6	14
Resistivity (ohm cm)	10^5	10^5	10^5	10^5	10^5
Curie point (°C.)	135	250	380	460	550
Specific gravity	4·8	4·6	4·4	4·2	3·7

These are nominal figures and refer to conditions at 20° C. unless otherwise stated.

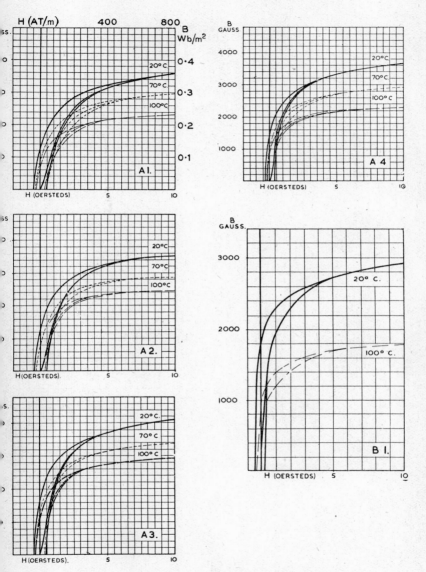

Fig. 2–39.—Typical B/H loops for ferroxcube "A" and "B1" grades.

(*Mullard Ltd.*)

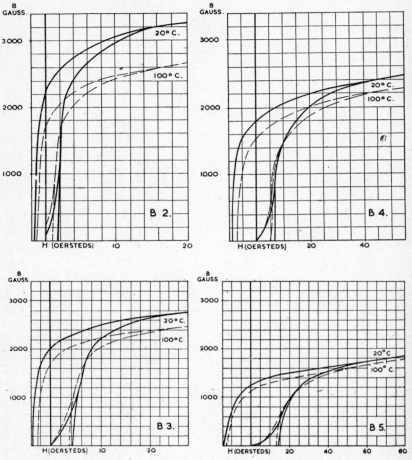

Fig. 2–39 (*continued*).—TYPICAL B/H LOOPS FOR FERROXCUBE B2, B3, B4 AND B5 GRADES.

(Mullard Ltd.)

The initial permeability is also subject to variation according to working temperature.

Curie Point

The initial permeability depends to a large extent upon the temperature, increasing at first as the temperature is raised, then decreasing very rapidly at a temperature of 150° C. to 190° C. for

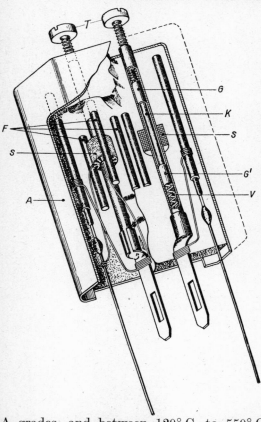

Fig. 2–40.—SECTIONAL ARRANGEMENT OF I.F. TRANSFORMER.

S = coils, K = Ferroxcube cores, adjustable by means of screws T and glass rods G. The cores are held in position by glass rods G' and springs V. Ferroxcube rods F constitute a so-called "palisade" screen for reducing losses in the aluminium can A. The components on the extreme right- and left-hand sides are "drawn" wire capacitors.

(*Philips Electrical Ltd.*)

A grades, and between 120° C. to 550° C. for B grades. The temperature at which the initial permeability falls to 10 per cent. of its maximum value is known as the Curie point. Ferroxcube cores should not, in general, be operated too close to the Curie temperature, although no permanent harm to the core results from uniform heating above this temperature.

MECHANICAL PROPERTIES

Ferroxcube is a hard, black, non-porous material (not a bonded powder core) of a ceramic nature, chemically inert and unaffected by humidity and other atmospheric conditions, with mechanical properties similar to those of the more common insulating ceramics. Although not easily broken, it should be handled with care, particularly to avoid chipping of sharp edges or corners.

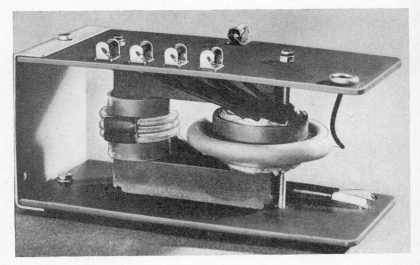

Fig. 2–41.—HIGH-EFFICIENCY TELEVISION RECEIVER LINE OUTPUT TRANSFORMER
USING MULLARD FERROXCUBE FERRITE " U " CORES.

(*Mullard Ltd.*)

Fig. 2–42.—MODERN HIGH-EFFICIENCY MAGNETIC TELEVISION RECEIVER
DEFLECTOR-COIL ASSEMBLY USING MULLARD FERROXCUBE CORES (SHOWN
ON RIGHT).

(*Mullard Ltd.*)

The table below gives the mechanical properties of Ferrox-cube which in general apply to all grades.

Specific gravity	4·8 for A grades.
	4·75 to 3·7 for B grades.
Young's modulus	21 × 10⁶ lb/sq. in.
Coefficient of linear expansion .	10⁻⁵ per °C.
Tensile strength	2,600 lb/sq. in.
Crushing strength . . .	10,400 lb/sq. in.
Specific heat	0·17 cal/gm/°C.
Thermal conductivity . .	8 × 10⁻³ cal/cm sec./°C.

The processed raw materials are milled into a finely divided powder, mixed in the correct proportions, and pressed to shape in dies, or extruded in the form of rods and tubes, and then sintered in a suitable atmosphere in a high-temperature furnace.

Shape of Pressings

Pressings should be of a fairly simple shape to facilitate the manufacture of dies, and abrupt changes in the section of the pressing should be avoided where possible. Slots and bevels can be provided in the piece part where they run parallel to the direction of pressing, and provided they do not materially reduce the section so as to make the pressing mechanically unsound. A uniform cross-section ensures a more satisfactory and consistent piece part with consequent less distortion after the firing operation.

Where large quantities of a given pressed part are required, automatic dies are used which are capable of providing a large output of piece parts of consistent shape ; but where initial samples are required to enable experiments to be carried out in order to prove or finalize a design, hand tools are used which enable only a limited number of piece parts to be produced. For samples, the making of dies can sometimes be avoided by fabricating a piece part from an existing die, shaping approximately to the required size before firing, and then grinding to the final dimensions.

Machining Operations

After the piece-parts have been sintered, they cannot be machined except by grinding, although they can be slit with diamond impregnated slitting wheels, or by ultrasonic methods. Due to the brittle and hard nature of the material, the large shrinkage—some 22 per cent., and the high sintering temperature, inserts of any description cannot be moulded into the pressed or extruded piece parts. It is, however, possible to thread rods and tubes externally.

Where two faces are to be butted together, grinding of the faces can be satisfactorily achieved by using abrasives of the aluminium oxide type. During the grinding operation light cuts only should be taken to avoid splintering sharp edges, and the piece part should be flooded with a coolant to avoid local heating which might cause cracking of the piece part.

Ferroxcube piece parts can be cemented together very successfully by most of the synthetic resin cements already in use with ceramics.

APPLICATIONS

Carrier-Telephony

Ferroxcube may be used as a core for filter coils used in carrier telephony. In these coils losses must be small in order to ensure sharp separation between the pass and attenuation bands. Flux density must be low to avoid distortion and a third requirement is that the coils must be of the smallest possible dimensions.

Other applications in telephony are for the cores of loading coils and wide band high-frequency transformers used in amplifiers in carrier-telephony systems. Here the main requirements are a flat response curve throughout a wide band of frequencies, low output impedance, and low overall losses.

Radio and Television

Recently, Ferroxcube has been used successfully in the manufacture of radio components, an example of this being intermediate frequency transformers (Fig. 2–40).

Amongst the several applications in television equipment may be mentioned the use of Ferroxcube in the apparatus used to generate the extra high-tension required for operating cathode-ray tubes (Fig. 2–41) and also for the cores of television-receiver deflector coils (Fig. 2–42).

3. (a) PERMANENT MAGNET STEELS AND ALLOYS

By

F. Knight, A.M.I.E.E.

The remarkable advances made in permanent magnet technique during the last 50 years probably surpass those made by any other trade or art in their relative magnitude. At the beginning of the century the only material available for the manufacture of permanent magnets was carbon tool steel. An indication of the advances made up to the present day is that the latest commercially available alloys are capable of producing an energy equivalent to about 40 times that of this earliest steel.

New Alloys

Whilst the advances made have been generally in the direction of steadily increasing energies, parallel investigations have produced alloys having special characteristics for particular applications.

This rapid expansion has resulted in a very wide range of materials suitable for permanent magnets being at the disposal of the designer and user. Contrary to what might have been expected, the newer alloys have not altogether replaced their forerunners, of which it is true to say that none has been completely displaced, each retaining its own sphere of application. This is not due to conservatism on the part of user or manufacturer but to the fact that for certain applications the earlier and less efficient magnet materials may give an overall economy when used in conjunction with a particular piece of equipment. Moreover, the intractability of some of the most modern alloys sometimes imposes physical and mechanical difficulties which make their use impracticable.

Classification of Permanent Magnet Materials

This wide range of permanent magnet materials can be subdivided into three main groups, which are discussed at length below. They are the carbide-bearing magnet steels, the compositions and performances of which have been long established and may, therefore, be regarded as standardized ; the diffusion-hardening alloys—the Alni, Alnico, Ticonal, Alcomax materials ; and the precipitation-hardening materials, which are of importance because of their ease of machinability. Many other materials exist which exhibit permanent magnetic properties, but only those are mentioned which are commercially available.

CARBIDE-BEARING MAGNET STEELS

This group of materials comprises all those which can be called magnet steels, being essentially carbon steels with added elements. Carbides formed during heat treatment produce high intermolecular stresses, which are responsible for their magnetic hardness.

The first special magnet steel to be developed was 6 per cent. tungsten steel. It represented quite a considerable advance magnetically over carbon steel. Chromium steel, containing up to 6 per cent. of chromium, originally a substitute material for tungsten, has retained its own sphere of usefulness in spite of its slightly reduced performance.

A more recent development is 2 per cent. cobalt/4 per cent. chromium steel. It has an increased performance and in spite of its rather different magnetic characteristics can often be substituted with advantage for tungsten steel in existing magnet designs.

Honda's original discovery in 1920 [1] of 35 per cent. cobalt magnet steel was followed by the development in England of a whole range of cobalt-bearing steels. These have been more or less standardized and manufacturers now usually supply steels containing 3, 6, 9, 15 or 35 per cent. of cobalt. The performances of these steels increase with the percentage of cobalt and, together with those mentioned earlier, they make a range of steels having energies in increasing steps from 2,400 J/m^3 (0·3 mega-gauss-oersteds (m.g.o.)) to 7,600 J/m^3 (0·95 m.g.o.) and coercivities from 0·53 × 10^4 A/m (66 oersteds) to 2 × 10^4 A/m (250 oersteds). Table 1 lists the magnetic properties of these steels.

DIFFUSION-HARDENING ALLOYS

Mishima discovered in 1931 [2] that an alloy of iron, nickel and aluminium approximating to the formula Fe_2NiAl had, after a suitable heat treatment, a coercivity about twice as great as that of 35 per cent. cobalt steel. The remanence was low, being just more than half that of the older steel and, as was to be

TABLE 1. AVERAGE MAGNETIC CHARACTERISTICS OF MAGNET STEELS

Material	Remanence	$(BH)_{max}$	Coercivity	B at $(BH)_{max}$	H at $(BH)_{max}$	Average recoil permeability	Maximum useful recoil energy	B at max. recoil point	H at max. recoil point
Symbol	B_{rem}		H_c	B_m	H_m	μ_r			
Unit	Wb/m²	J/m³	A/m	Wb/m²	A/m		J/m³	Wb/m²	A/m
6 per cent. Tungsten	1·05 (10,500)	2,380 (0·3)	×10⁴ 0·525 (66)	0·7 (7,000)	×10⁴ 0·342 (43)	49 × 10⁻⁶ (39)	763 (0·096)	0·725 (7,250)	×10⁴ 0·191 (24)
Chromium	0·98 (9,800)	2,270 (0·285)	0·557 (70)	0·62 (6,200)	0·366 (46)	44 × 10⁻⁶ (35)	735 (0·0925)	0·620 (6,200)	0·207 (26)
2 per cent. Cobalt, 4 per cent. Chromium	0·98 (9,800)	2,540 (0·32)	0·636 (80)	0·628 (6,280)	0·406 (51)	37·7 × 10⁻⁶ (30)	831 (0·1045)	0·630 (6,300)	0·231 (29)
3 per cent. Cobalt	0·72 (7,200)	2,780 (0·35)	1·03 (130)	0·425 (4,250)	0·652 (82)	23·2 × 10⁻⁶ (18·5)	970 (0·122)	0·410 (4,100)	0·390 (49)
6 per cent. Cobalt	0·75 (7,500)	3,500 (0·44)	1·15 (145)	0·47 (4,700)	0·748 (94)	22 × 10⁻⁶ (17·5)	1,230 (0·155)	0·485 (4,850)	0·422 (53)
9 per cent. Cobalt	0·78 (7,800)	3,980 (0·50)	1·27 (160)	0·50 (5,000)	0·796 (100)	20·7 × 10⁻⁶ (16·5)	1,390 (0·175)	0·500 (5,000)	0·470 (59)
15 per cent. Cobalt	0·82 (8,200)	4,930 (0·62)	1·43 (180)	0·525 (5,250)	0·938 (118)	18·8 × 10⁻⁶ (15)	1,710 (0·215)	0·530 (5,300)	0·540 (68)
35 per cent. Cobalt	0·90 (9,000)	7,560 (0·95)	1·99 (250)	0·593 (5,930)	1·27 (160)	15·1 × 10⁻⁶ (12)	2,630 (0·331)	0·585 (5,850)	0·748 (94)

Note. In this and other Tables all magnetic values are given in units of the rationalized M.K.S. system, the corresponding values in C.G.S. units being shown bracketed. Energy values are given in $(B \times H)$ units, the M.K.S. values being in Joules/metre³ and the C.G.S. values being in mega-gauss-oersteds.

TABLE 2.   AVERAGE MAGNETIC CHARACTERISTICS OF ISOTROPIC DIFFUSION-HARDENING ALLOYS

Material	Remanence	$(BH)_{max}$	Coercivity	B at $(BH)_{max}$	H at $(BH)_{max}$	Average recoil permeability	Maximum useful recoil energy	B at max. recoil point	H at max. recoil point
Symbol	B_{rem}	$(BH)_{max}$	H_c	B_m	H_m	μ_r			
Unit	Wb/m²	J/m³	A/m $\times 10^4$	Wb/m²	A/m $\times 10^4$		J/m³	Wb/m²	A/m $\times 10^4$
Alni (high remanence)	0·62 (6,200)	9,950 (1·25)	3·82 (480)	0·402 (4,020)	2·47 (311)	$6·91 \times 10^{-6}$ (5·5)	3,800 (0·477)	0·40 (4,000)	1·58 (198)
Alni (normal)	0·56 (5,600)	9,950 (1·25)	4·61 (580)	0·348 (3,480)	2·86 (360)	$6·28 \times 10^{-6}$ (5·0)	4,250 (0·534)	0·342 (3,420)	1·85 (232)
Alni (high coercivity)	0·50 (5,000)	9,950 (1·25)	5·41 (680)	0·304 (3,040)	3·26 (410)	$5·03 \times 10^{-6}$ (4·0)	4,330 (0·544)	0·292 (2,920)	2·16 (272)
Alnico (high remanence)	0·80 (8,000)	13,500 (1·70)	3·98 (500)	0·531 (5,310)	2·54 (320)	$8·8 \times 10^{-6}$ (7·0)	5,170 (0·650)	0·510 (5,100)	1·59 (200)
Alnico (normal)	0·725 (7,250)	13,500 (1·70)	4·46 (560)	0·472 (4,720)	2·86 (360)	$7·54 \times 10^{-6}$ (6·0)	5,360 (0·674)	0·465 (4,650)	1·79 (225)
Alnico (high coercivity)	0·65 (6,500)	13,500 (1·70)	4·93 (620)	0·425 (4,250)	3·18 (400)	$6·53 \times 10^{-6}$ (5·2)	5,470 (0·688)	0·432 (4,320)	1·96 (246)
Reco 2A	0·52 (5,200)	12,300 (1·55)	6·96 (875)	—	—	—	—	—	—
Hynico II	0·55 (5,500)	12,700 (1·60)	7·16 (900)	0·314 (3,140)	4·06 (510)	$5·03 \times 10^{-6}$ (4·0)	7,080 (0·890)	0·248 (2,480)	3·3 (415)

expected, the $(BH)_{max}$ value was only slightly higher. However, the economic advantage from using an alloy containing cheaper base elements was very great and intensive research work on alloys of similar composition was carried out.

Improved properties were obtained in Britain, and in 1933 the alloy known as Alni was marketed. Basically similar to the Mishima invention, Alni has an internal energy some 25 per cent. greater than that of 35 per cent. cobalt and, by slight variation of composition, the coercivity may be varied between the wide limits given in Table 2.

Further research in Britain [3] led to the discovery of Alnico. Based on the earlier work on iron-nickel-aluminium alloys, Alnico also contains cobalt and copper which together have the effect of increasing the remanence without reducing the coercivity. An energy increase of approximately 40 per cent. over the performance of Alni was achieved with this alloy and, again, variation of characteristics can be obtained by careful control of composition. The coercivity may be varied between similar limits, i.e. 4×10^4 A/m to 5×10^4 A/m (500–620 oersteds), and corresponding remanences of from $0 \cdot 8$ Wb/m^2 to $0 \cdot 65$ Wb/m^2 (8,000 gauss to 6,500 gauss) are obtained.

The special alloys Hynico II and Reco 2A are recent developments to satisfy the requirement for an Alnico type of material having very high coercivity coupled with a $(BH)_{max}$ product of the same order. They find application where the permissible magnetic length is restricted by other considerations, as in small generator rotors having four or more magnetic poles.

Anisotropic Alloys

In 1938, an experiment was carried out by Oliver and Shedden [4] which has proved to have been a milestone in the history of the development of permanent magnet alloys. They found that if the cooling of Alnico from the high-temperature solution treatment (1,250° C) took place in the presence of a magnetic field strength of the order of 24×10^4 A/m (3,000 oersteds) it became magnetically anisotropic. Its properties in the direction of the applied field were improved at the expense of those in other directions, the internal energy increase being of the order of 10 to 15 per cent. above that of specimens having similar heat treatments but without the application of the magnetic field.

TABLE 3.   AVERAGE * MAGNETIC CHARACTERISTICS OF ANISOTROPIC DIFFUSION-HARDENING ALLOYS

Material	Remanence B_{rem}	$(BH)_{max}$	Coercivity H_c	B at $(BH)_{max}$ B_m	H at $(BH)_{max}$ H_m	Average useful recoil permeability μ_r	Maximum recoil energy	B at max. recoil point	H at max. recoil point
Symbol / Unit	Wb/m²	J/m³	A/m	Wb/m²	A/m		J/m³	Wb/m²	A/m
Alcomax II	1·24 (12,400)	35,800 (4·5)	× 10⁴ 4·57 (575)	0·99 (9,900)	× 10⁴ 3·62 (455)	3·77 × 10⁻⁶ (3·0)	10,250 (1·29)	1·019 (10,190)	× 10⁴ 1·88 (237)
Ticonal G	1·27 (12,700)	39,800 (5·0)*	5·09 (640)	—	—	—	—	—	—
Alcomax III	1·25 (12,500)	39,800 (5·0)*	5·33 (670)	0·968 (9,680)	4·1 (516)	4·4 × 10⁻⁶ (3·5)	11,900 (1·50)	1·005 (10,050)	2·17 (273)
Alcomax IV	1·12 (11,200)	34,200 (4·3)	5·96 (750)	0·8 (8,000)	4·27 (537)	5·03 × 10⁻⁶ (4·0)	11,100 (1·40)	0·812 (8,120)	2·40 (302)
Hycomax	0·9 (9,000)	25,400 (3·2)	6·56 (825)	0·593 (5,930)	4·3 (540)	5·65 × 10⁻⁶ (4·5)	9,620 (1·21)	0·615 (6,150)	2·52 (317)

* See p. 102,

The significance of this performance improvement did not escape the notice of other workers, and the logical investigation of other alloys of similar composition which followed led to the development in 1940 in Holland of the alloy Ticonal [5] and in Britain of Alcomax I.[6] It was discovered that alloys having a higher cobalt content than ordinary Alnico could be made surprisingly anisotropic, the order of improvement due to the application of a magnetic field during heat treatment being increased from 15 to 200 per cent. Further composition modifications and improvements in manufacturing technique produced improved versions of these alloys, namely Alcomax II [7] and Ticonal G.[8]

Continued research into these complex alloys resulted in the development of the alloy Hycomax,[9] which has a high coercivity of the order of 70,000 A/m (875 oersteds); unfortunately, this was obtained at the expense of a reduction in contained energy. This alloy has only a limited application to special designs in which the magnet is subjected to high demagnetizing forces or in which physical or mechanical considerations limit the permissible length of magnet.

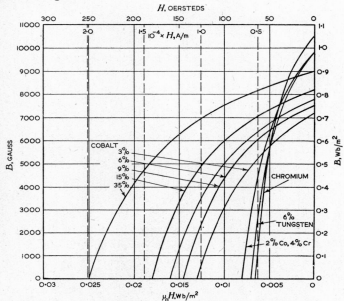

Fig. 3–1.—DEMAGNETIZATION CURVES OF MAGNET STEELS.

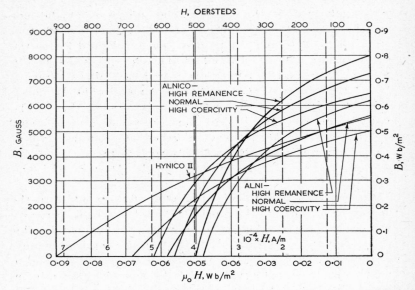

Fig. 3–2.—DEMAGNETIZATION CURVES OF ISOTROPIC DIFFUSION HARDENING ALLOYS.

Improvement in magnetic energy of the anisotropic alloys could logically be expected only by increase in coercivity, since their remanences approach the saturation density. It was found in 1950 that additions of niobium (columbium) or tantalum or both were beneficial when added to alloys of the Alcomax II or Ticonal types and had the effect of increasing the coercivity without reducing the contained energy. Two new materials were marketed following this development : Alcomax III [10] with very high energy and Alcomax IV [11] with very high coercivity.

The magnetic characteristics of the isotropic and anisotropic diffusion-hardening alloys are given in Tables 2 and 3 respectively. As with all magnetic materials, the number of variables affecting the magnetic characteristics is high, resulting in a fairly wide spread of performance between individual magnets. In listing the magnetic properties an attempt has been made to give the average values likely to be obtained from magnets not presenting any serious production problems. Figs. 3–1, 3–2 and 3–3 give the demagnetization curves to which the listed characteristics refer.

Columnar Crystal Magnets

By careful control of the cooling of diffusion-hardening alloys from the molten condition, selective orientation of the crystal structure may be achieved. It has been found that with the correct crystal arrangement the anisotropic alloys within this range of materials can be made to have phenomenal properties far exceeding those obtained by normal manufacturing methods.

A sufficient cooling differential between the sides and base of a casting causes a preponderance of crystals to grow from the base. If a proportion of such crystals exceeding 75 per cent. of the whole of the casting can be made to grow throughout the height, improved properties may be obtained with the anisotropic alloys by making the subsequent heat-treatment magnetization in the direction of the columnar formation. The difficulties of production are great and the principle has not yet found extensive commercial application. The limitations on size and proportions

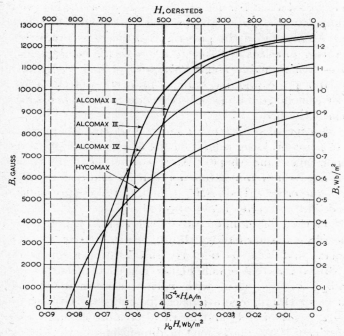

Fig. 3–3.—DEMAGNETIZATION CURVES ANISOTROPIC DIFFUSION HARDENING ALLOYS.

of magnets made by the method are severe and the costs of production at present are high.

The magnetic characteristics obtained in production are dependent largely upon the shape and proportions of the magnet, and whilst energies of over 63,500 J/m³ (8·0 m.g.o.) have been obtained on laboratory-prepared samples, an average result of 49,700 J/m³ (6·25 m.g.o.) can be obtained from an ideal shape. The best results can be expected from magnets of cylindrical section of approximately 1 sq. in. and a length not exceeding ¾ in.

Materials made by this method are marketed under the trade names of Alnico D.G. (U.S.A.) and Columax (Great Britain).

Sintered Magnets

The well-known sintering method of manufacture of hard metals has been applied with considerable success to the manufacture of permanent magnets in materials of the diffusion-hardening type. The various constituent metals, crushed to 200-mesh powders of balanced particle distribution, are mixed according to the composition required and pressed into moulds of the desired shape.[12] Sintering of the pressing so formed is carried out at a temperature upwards of 1,350° C in a reducing atmosphere. This produces a hardenable magnet shape of a high order of homogenity and possessing mechanical properties often superior to those of cast magnets, undoubtedly due to the much finer grain structure obtained.

The density of a sintered magnet material is approximately 10 to 15 per cent. lower than the corresponding cast alloy, depending upon mass and shape. After correct heat treatment this results in a reduction in saturation density and residual induction of the same order. The $(BH)_{max}$, or internal energy, is similarly reduced, but coercivity is not affected.

This method of manufacture is successfully applied to most of the diffusion-hardening alloys, Alnico, Alcomax, Ticonal, Hycomax, and it is particularly suitable for magnets of very small dimensions. A much higher degree of accuracy is quite naturally obtained than with normal sand-moulded magnets, and often machining operations can be omitted. Greater freedom of design is permissible and magnets of more complicated shape are possible ; large variations in dimensions in the direction of pressing are undesirable, however.

The production costs of sintered magnets are comparatively high, and generally the method offers economic advantage only when the weight of the magnet does not exceed 20 gm. The average weight of magnets made by the process is considerably less than this.

Sintering involves the use of expensive tools and is economically practicable when quantities of 10,000 or more of a particular design are required. The difficulty which this imposes upon development and prototype production is overcome, either by the machining of one of the many designs for which tools exist or by cutting the shape required from a standard block before the sintering operation.

PRECIPITATION-HARDENING ALLOYS

The group of alloys listed, with their approximate compositions and magnetic characteristics, in Table 4 have been developed during the years 1931 to 1946, mainly in the U.S.A., where they have found limited application because of the ease with which they can be machined and cold worked, sometimes even in the magnetically hard condition. They are expensive to produce, and probably this and the fact that in general their magnetic properties are no higher than those of 35 per cent. cobalt steel are responsible for the lack of serious development of them in Britain and elsewhere.

Comol, Comalloy, or Remalloy, as it is variously called, is a useful precipitation-hardening alloy having magnetic characteristics very similar to those of 35 per cent. cobalt steel. However, it offers little advantage over the older steel for which the manufacturing technique is long established, and consequently has not been seriously developed in Britain.

The Cunife alloys I and II—copper-nickel-iron and copper-nickel-iron-cobalt—are easily worked even in the magnetically hard state. They are made anisotropic by heavy cold working, and the $(BH)_{max}$ in the direction of rolling may reach a value as high as 14,700 J/m³ (1·85 m.g.o.).

Alloys of copper, nickel and cobalt—the American Cunico I and II materials—have contained energies rather lower than those of 35 per cent. cobalt steel, and are easily worked. Relatively low energy values and high cost have prevented the serious exploitation of these iron-free alloys.

H

TABLE 4. COMPOSITION, MAGNETIC AND MECHANICAL PROPERTIES OF PRECIPITATION-HARDENING ALLOYS

Material	Composition by weight (per cent.)						Magnetic properties				Mechanical properties
	N_1	Co	Cu	Mo	V	Fe	Remanence B_{rem} Wb/m²	$(BH)_{max}$ J/m³	Coercivity H_c A/m	Density gm./cm.³	
Comalloy · ·	—	12	—	17	—	bal.	1·0 (10,000)	7,960 (1·0)	$\times 10^4$ 1·83 (230)	8·1	Brittle but machinable.
Cunife I · ·	20	—	60	—	—	bal.	0·57 (5,700)	14,700 (1·85)	4·69 (590)	8·6	Ductile.
Cunife II · ·	20	2·5	50	—	—	bal.	0·73 (7,300)	6,200 (0·78)	2·07 (260)	8·6	Ductile.
Cunico I · ·	21	29	50	—	—	—	0·34 (3,400)	6,760 (0·85)	5·64 (710)	8·3	Ductile.
Cunico II · ·	24	41	35	—	—	—	0·53 (5,300)	7,870 (0·99)	3·58 (450)	8·3	Ductile.
Vicalloy I · ·	—	52	—	—	10	bal.	0·9 (9,000)	7,960 (1·00)	2·38 (300)	—	Ductile.
Vicalloy II · ·	—	52	—	—	13	bal.	1·0 (10,000)	2,390 (3·00)	3·58 (450)	—	Ductile.

TABLE 5. COMPOSITION AND MECHANICAL PROPERTIES PERMANENT MAGNET STEELS AND ALLOYS

Material	Composition, weight per cent. approx. balance, Iron										Density, gm./cm.^{3}	Hardness, Rockwell "C"	Mechanical properties	Method of manufacture
	Al	C	Cr	Co	Cu	Mo	Ni	Nb (Cb)	Ti	W				
Chromium steel	—	0·9	3·5	—	—	—	—	—	—	—	7·7	62		
6 per cent. Tungsten steel	—	0·7	0·3	—	—	—	—	—	—	6·0	8·1	63		
2 per cent. Cobalt, 4 per cent. Chromium steel	—	1·0	4·0	2·0	—	—	—	—	—	0·5	7·8	60	Strong — forgeable. Machinable after annealing.	Cast as individual magnets or as ingots for hot rolling and subsequent forging and/or machining.
3 per cent. Cobalt steel	—	1·0	9·0	3·0	—	1·5	—	—	—	—	7·7	62		
6 per cent. Cobalt steel	—	1·0	9·0	6·0	—	1·5	—	—	—	—	7·75	62		
9 per cent. Cobalt steel	—	1·0	9·0	9·0	—	1·5	—	—	—	—	7·8	63		
15 per cent. Cobalt steel	—	1·0	9·0	15·0	—	1·5	—	—	—	—	7·9	64	Brittle — forgeable. Machinable with difficulty after annealing.	
35 per cent. Cobalt steel	—	0·9	6·0	35·0	—	—	—	—	—	5·0	8·15	62		
Alni	12–13	—	—	—	—	—	24–32	—	0–0·5	—	6·9	50	Brittle.	Cast individual magnets—grind to fine dimensions.
Alnico	8–11	—	—	12	6	—	17–20	—	—	—	7·4	54	Extremely brittle.	
Hynico II	8·5	—	—	18	4	—	20	1	4	—	7·2	54		
Reco 2A	8·0	—	—	11	6	—	24	—	5	—	—	—		
Alcomax II	8·0	—	—	21	4·5	—	11·5	—	—	—	7·5	54		
Ticonal G	8·0	—	—	24	3·0	—	14	—	—	—	7·5	—	Brittle.	—Sinter
Alcomax III	8·0	—	—	24	3·0	—	13·5	0·75	—	—	7·5	52		
Hycomax	9·0	—	—	20	2·0	—	21	—	—	—	7·3	—		
Alcomax IV	8·0	—	—	24	3·0	—	13·5	3·0	—	—	7·5	55		

H 2

The cobalt-iron-vanadium alloys Vicalloy I and Vicalloy II are two further examples of this class of material. Heavy cold working produces a high degree of anisotropy in the direction of rolling, and energies as high as 23,800 J/m³ (3·0 m.g.o.) have been recorded for small sections such as 0·020-in. tape or wire. The very high cobalt and vanadium contents make them very expensive alloys and the application is limited : there has been no serious commercial manufacture in Great Britain.

MECHANICAL AND PHYSICAL PROPERTIES OF P.M. MATERIALS

An understanding of the mechanical and physical limitations of the various special magnet steels and alloys which have been discussed is most important in view of the limitations which these properties impose on the design and application of magnets.

Whilst magnetic hardness is by no means synonymous with physical hardness, it is nevertheless true to say that, with those materials finding the greatest commercial application, good magnetic properties often go hand in hand with physical weakness. This is not altogether surprising when viewed in the light of the modern concept of magnetic hardness and high coercivity being due to high internal strain.

The general physical properties of magnet steels and alloys are given briefly in Tables 4 and 5 and are detailed more fully below. The various methods of manufacture are also given.

Carbide-bearing Magnet Steels

The tungsten, chromium and cobalt steels have good physical and mechanical properties. They may be manufactured by the normal steel-making processes of casting into ingot form followed by subsequent cogging and rolling to the required section, or alternatively, when very complicated magnet shapes are required, these may be made by pouring from the shank into individual sand moulds. Forging of rolled bars into the " U " or " C " magnet shapes which are common for magnets in these materials is usual practice, and presents no serious difficulties to those versed in the art.

Machining by normal methods is possible in a fully annealed state (720°–740° C, slowly cooled) although very small drilled and tapped holes are to be avoided, particularly in the higher grades of cobalt. The 35 per cent. cobalt steel is the most brittle of this group of steels and, to minimize the danger of cracking during heat treatment, rapid changes of section in castings and sharp corners in forgings are undesirable.

The Diffusion-hardening Alloys

The highly crystalline nature of the Alni, Alnico, Alcomax and Ticonal alloys causes them to have comparatively low mechanical strength. Manipulation by normal steel-making methods— rolling, forging, etc.—is not possible, and magnets have to be cast to the approximate final shape in individual sand moulds. The hard, brittle nature of these materials prevents normal machining methods, and consequently the shape must permit grinding to the required form. Considerable ingenuity is used in modern magnet foundries to produce the small and difficult shapes sometimes required, and individual sand castings of less than only 10 gm. weight are economically manufactured in very large quantities. A limited amount of drilling is possible after prolonged annealing of some of these alloys, but it is a difficult operation and is to be avoided where possible. Accurately positioned holes may be provided by the grinding of holes cored in the casting or for very small holes a larger, cored hole can be filled with soft metal and drilled to the size required.

The Precipitation-hardening Alloys

Magnets in these materials are usually machined from the rolled- or drawn-bar stock ; indeed, as has already been stated, with certain of them extensive cold working is necessary to produce optimum magnetic properties. In quite a number of cases manipulation and machining is possible in the magnetically hard state.

Comalloy tends to be brittle although machinable, and care must be taken during manipulation to avoid cracking. Magnets may be made from rolled bar or as castings.

THE PHYSICAL AND MECHANICAL ASPECTS OF PERMANENT MAGNET DESIGN

The physical properties of permanent magnet alloys have been dealt with elsewhere. The problems met in the use of the available alloys and methods of assembly and construction are discussed here.

Magnetic design considerations establish the dimensions of length and sectional area of a magnet. These tend to be inversely proportional to the values of H_c and B_r respectively, and thus magnets in the older types of steel are long and of small section whereas magnets in Alni or Alnico tend to be of short length but of greater cross-section. Alcomax or Ticonal magnets of optimum design and for given performances are of similar length to corresponding ones in Alnico but have a sectional area of less than half.

These very general considerations will give an indication of the general trend of magnet shape and proportions in those cases where the older steels have been replaced by the more modern alloys. It is an indication only because the newer alloys, having higher magnet energies, have made possible higher overall performances, and magnet dimensions have not been reduced in an inverse proportion to the increased internal energies (see p. 114).

It will be obvious after study of magnetic design considerations that theoretically any air-gap performance can be achieved using any of the wide range of alloys and steels. However, from practical considerations, it will be obvious that this is not so. The overall space available in many pieces of apparatus requiring high magnetic energies prevents the use of correctly designed magnets in the older low-performance steels. On the other hand, mechanical considerations sometimes fix the length of a magnet approximately, and if this should be much greater than the optimum for one of the newer alloys, it is possible that a lower coercivity material will be more efficient and economical.

The choice of material can be made only after a study of all the factors involved and the calculation of optimum dimensions in several materials.

Methods of Production

The methods of production of magnet steels allow a considerable latitude in the choice of design. Their machinability and comparatively high strength are such that the mounting of pole pieces or the fixing of the magnet into its associated equipment is comparatively simple by normal engineering techniques, provided that the reservations made regarding tapped holes in the higher cobalt steels are borne in mind.

With any of the nickel-aluminium or nickel-aluminium-cobalt alloys the inherent brittleness and low physical strength must be allowed for in design. Whereas with the magnet steels it is permissible to mount associated parts on to the magnet this is not so with the newer alloys.

The shape of magnets in these materials must permit of moulding in sand, and for ease of production complicated designs requiring the insertion of cores should be avoided where possible. Rapid changes of section are undesirable, since these are liable to cause subsequent cracking in heat treatment.

Small holes in castings are a source of trouble, and a length/ diameter ratio of not more than four is desirable ; where possible, external slots should be used instead, since these can be positioned more accurately. Such slots permit the use of clamping bolts to fix the brittle magnet to its pole pieces or housing.

Various other methods of assembly other than by the clamping of the magnet are possible. It is common practice to mould a magnet, together with any associated pole pieces, into a pressure die-casting using a non-magnetic zinc-base alloy. This method is particularly suitable for the rotors of alternators or magnetos, where the magnet pole pieces are often laminated, and sometimes the whole assembly can be moulded around a shaft, final machining being carried out after die-casting. With the alloys of low-temperature melting-point which are used, the heat transference to the magnet is not sufficient to affect the magnetic properties. A particular advantage of such methods of assembly, especially with rotating parts, is that the low mechanical strength of the magnet becomes of quite secondary importance since it is completely encased.

Pressing of magnets into pole pieces is possible, but is advisable only if the stresses to which the magnet is subjected are compressive. The pressing of shafts into the ground bores of rotor magnets is deprecated, since the stresses created may be sufficient to cause cracking, which does not necessarily occur immediately.

Brazing is a practicable method of assembly provided that a low-temperature brazing medium is used so that the magnet is not overheated. High-frequency methods are admirable, since the heat can be localized. Soft soldering is also possible, the great difficulty being the adequate cleaning of the surfaces. This can sometimes be overcome by copper plating the parts to be joined.

Fastening by means of synthetic resin adhesives is a practicable method of assembly, but the method is usually restricted to magnets of small dimensions. Where the magnet block is suitably encased, positioning by means of a low-melting-point alloy, sulphur, or a thermosetting plastic medium, is sometimes adequate. Such methods are often used for the fixing of spindles into the central cored hole of small alternator rotor magnets.

Where unit construction of pole pieces is employed, magnetic attraction is often sufficient to retain the magnet. This is particularly so with the high-performance anisotropic alloys having a high working flux density (Pull α B^2), and when the magnet dimensions are small.

PERMANENT MAGNET DESIGN

A permanent magnet invariably works under conditions of demagnetization caused by the field it establishes in the surrounding space or in an air-gap forming part of a more clearly defined magnetic circuit. The sense or direction of the gap field is opposite to that of the field inside the magnet, which is consequently partially demagnetized. An examination of the hysteresis loop diagram (Fig. 3–4) shows that the conditions under which the magnet maintains a positive flux under demagnetization occur when the working point lies in the upper left-hand quadrant. The magnet flux density falls as the demagnetizing force increases, but in the absence of any externally applied magnetization the working condition cannot fall below the point ($-H = H_c$, $B = 0$).

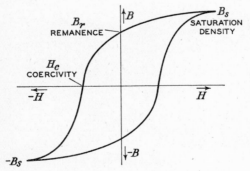

Fig. 3–4.—HYSTERESIS LOOP SHOWING PRINCIPLE POINTS.

When the magnet supplies a static flux with no recoil, the working point of the flux density within the magnet falls from the initial density B_s to a point on the demagnetization curve at which $- H$, the demagnetizing field per unit magnet length, is sufficient to meet the demands of flux-maintenance in the external circuit.

Let a uniform gap of length L_g be cut in a magnet-ring having the hysteresis loop partly shown in Fig. 3–5. Suppose the working point is N, corresponding to a magnet flux density B_1 and a demagnetizing field $- H_1$. If the magnet has a length L_m and a cross-section A_m, its flux will be $B_1 A_m$ and the m.m.f. released for the gap will be $H_1 L_m$.

The flux $B_1 A_m$ will, as a simple approximation, become $B_g A_g$

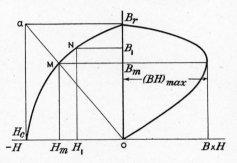

Fig. 3–5.—DEMAGNETIZATION AND ENERGY CURVES WITH GEOMETRICAL CONSTRUCTION FOR BH_{max}.

in the gap, if the gap area A_g is assumed to have a uniformly-distributed density B_g and leakage is neglected. Consequently

$$B_1 A_m = B_g A_g \text{ and } H_1 L_m = H_g L_g = B_g L_g / \mu_0 \quad . \quad . \quad (1)$$

These mean that the gap flux is the same as the magnet flux (which is a natural consequence of the circuital nature of magnetic flux) and that the m.m.f. released by the fall of magnet flux is applied to maintain that flux in the gap.

The energy W per unit volume of a gap permeated by a magnetic flux density B_g associated with a field strength H_g is

$$W = \tfrac{1}{2} B_g H_g = \tfrac{1}{2} B_g^2 / \mu_0.$$

For gap dimensions L_g and A_g the total energy W stored in the gap is

$$W = \tfrac{1}{2} B_g^2 A_g L_g / \mu_0$$
$$= \tfrac{1}{2} B_1 H_1 A_m L_m$$
$$= \tfrac{1}{2} (B_1 H_1) U_m \quad . \quad . \quad . \quad . \quad . \quad (2)$$

using the relations in equation (1) and writing the magnet volume as $A_m L_m = U_m$. Thus the stored energy in the gap corresponds to that released by the magnet, and the product $\frac{1}{2}(B_1 H_1)$ is the gap energy produced per unit volume of magnet.

The $(BH)_{max}$ Point

A curve connecting the product (BH) with B has the characteristic shape shown to the right in Fig. 3–5. The value is zero for points B_r and H_c, and rises to a maximum intermediately. The position of this point, known as the $(BH)_{max}$ point, may be found from suitable measurements : it is a most important criterion of the usefulness of a permanent-magnet material.

For a rectangular hyperbola, to which most demagnetization curves closely approximate, this point of maximum energy is given by the intersection of the diagonal of the rectangle $aB_r O H_c$ in Fig. 3–5, with the demagnetization curve.

For a given air-gap energy, U_m will be a minimum when B_1 and H_1 are the co-ordinates of this maximum point : the most economical design using the least volume of magnet material will be obtained therefore if the working point of the magnet occurs at the $(BH)_{max}$ point.

The formulæ in equation (1) take no account of leakages occurring in practical magnet systems. The path of the magnet external flux is not confined to the gap, flux emanating from the whole surface of the magnet and not just from its pole faces or extremities. The amount of flux external to the air-gap, usually called leakage flux, is dependent upon the area and length of gap and the flux density within it. It increases as gap flux density and length increase and is reduced as the gap area is increased.

The integration of all the circuit reluctances is extremely difficult, and since with particular designs there exists a more or less constant ratio between the gap or useful reluctance and all the others, it is usual to make use of a leakage coefficient to simplify design. This assumption is further justified since in many designs by far the greater part of the flux leakage occurs in the immediate vicinity of the air-gap. Usually designated K_a, this leakage factor is equal to the total magnet flux divided by the gap or useful flux ($K_a = \Phi_m/\Phi_g$). This coefficient is by no means constant and it increases with increase of flux density in the air-gap. Its value varies very widely, being seldom less than

·5 even for very short gaps where the leakage is lowest, and rising to as much as 30 in extreme cases where the flux density is high and the gap length great. An example of how the leakage coefficient K_a varies as the flux density in the gap of a loudspeaker magnet is increased is shown in Fig. 3–6.

Effects of Small Gaps

It is customary to introduce a second coefficient into design formulæ to take into account the effects of small gaps at joints in the magnetic circuit, the reluctances of pole pieces and the curvature of lines of force within the actual gap. This coefficient K_l) is usually combined with the gap length in computing the

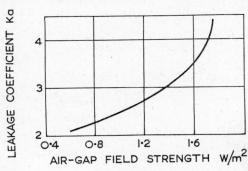

*Fig. 3–6.—*GRAPH SHOWING THE VARIATION OF THE SECTION LEAKAGE COEFFI-CIENT WITH FLUX DENSITY IN A LOUDSPEAKER MAGNET HAVING AN AIRGAP 1 IN. DIA. × 0·04 IN. LONG AND 0·187 IN. DEEP.

total gap m.m.f. It does not vary so widely as the leakage coefficient and is generally between 1·1 and 1·5.

In the practical case therefore equation (1) cannot be used since

$$\Phi_m = K_a \cdot \Phi_g$$

therefore

$$B_m \cdot A_m = B_g \cdot A_g \cdot K_a \quad \ldots \quad \ldots \quad (3)$$

similarly

$$H_m \cdot L_m = B_g \cdot L_g \cdot K_l \times 10^7/4\pi \quad \ldots \quad (4)$$

and

$$B_m \cdot H_m \cdot U_m = B_g{}^2 \cdot A_g \cdot L_g \cdot K_a \cdot K_l \times 10^7/4\pi \quad (5)$$

It is not possible to give methods for computing these widely varying coefficients, and it is generally only by pre-knowledge of a particular form of magnet that the design engineer is able to make an accurate estimate of their values. With unknown designs, whilst it is possible to calculate the reluctance of the various leakage paths and so to determine what flux will pass along them, probably the most satisfactory way is by careful measurement of fluxes within various parts of the magnetic circuit of an approximate prototype. Once these factors have

been established, the design of magnets to give a given per
formance within an air gap is a comparatively simple matter
using equations (3), (4) and (5).

Permeance Lines

The solution of design problems is facilitated if permeances ar
used as opposed to reluctances. The permeance P of a circuit i
the reciprocal of its reluctance S and is the sum of the individua
permeances of the various parts of the magnetic circuit.

Related to the magnet

$$P = 1/S = \Phi/\text{m.m.f.} = B_m \cdot A_m/H_m \cdot L_m \quad . \quad (6$$

Unit permeance,[13] p, or the permeance as seen from uni
volume of the magnet, is given by the equation

$$p = P \cdot L_m/A_m = B_m/H_m \quad . \quad . \quad . \quad . \quad (7$$

From equations (3) and (4)

$$B_m = B_g \cdot A_g \cdot K_a/A_m \text{ and } H_m = \frac{B_g \cdot L_g \cdot K_l \times 10^7}{L_m \times 4\pi}$$

so that

$$p = \frac{B_g \cdot A_g \cdot K_a \cdot L_m \times 4\pi}{B_g \cdot L_g \cdot K_l \cdot A_m \times 10^7}$$

and therefore

$$p = \frac{A_g \cdot L_m \cdot K_a}{L_g \cdot A_m \cdot K_l} \times \frac{4\pi}{10^7} \quad . \quad . \quad . \quad . \quad (8$$

For a given magnet design therefore the unit permeance is a
numerical constant which is independent of magnet charac
teristics. For a particular magnet design which is ideal, in that
the working point is the $(BH)_{max}$ point, it is equal to and passing
through B_m/H_m. A line drawn through the intersection of the I
and H axes at this point is known as a permeance line.

Once the permeance for a magnet design has been established
the effect on the performance due to a direct interchange of
magnets of different materials is easy to determine. In Fig. 3–7
the ideal permeance line passing through the $(BH)_{max}$ point for
Alnico, flux density 0.472 Wb/m², intersects the demagnetization
curve for Alcomax III at flux density 0.772 Wb/m². The magnet
working flux density is increased therefore from 0.472 to
0.772 Wb/m² and the gap flux would tend to be increased in the
same proportion. However, the internal energy of Alcomax III
at this particular point is only 3.62×10^4 J/m³ (4.54×10^6 m.g.o.)
whereas the maximum energy obtainable for an ideal design

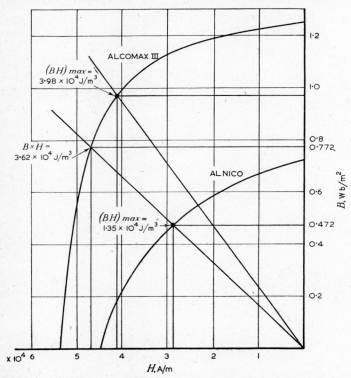

Fig. 3–7.—COMPARISON OF ALNICO AND ALCOMAX III SHOWING HOW THE PER-
MEANCE OF A MAGNET DESIGN MUST BE VARIED TO ACHIEVE THE MAXIMUM
UTILIZATION OF THE ALLOY.

is $3\cdot98 \times 10^4$ J/m³ ($5\cdot00 \times 10^6$ m.g.o) and therefore the most
economic utilization is not obtained. To give the highest efficiency
the magnet proportions would have to be altered until the
permeance was $2\cdot36 \times 10^{-5}$ ($B_m/H_m = 18\cdot8$ in the c.g.s. system).

Recoil Lines.   Reversible Permeability

If a magnet is subjected to a greater demagnetizing force than
that produced by the negative field of the air-gap the working
point N (Fig. 3–8) moves down the demagnetization curve to
some point N_1 determined by the new set of conditions.   This
occurs when the reluctance of the flux path is increased, as for
instance when the armature of a generator is removed from the
field magnet.   When the additional reluctance is removed (i.e.

when the armature is replaced) the flux density in the magnet does not recover along the original demagnetization curve but on a minor hysteresis loop (N_1QR in Fig. 3–8) to the value R where ORN is the normal working permeance line. The effect is reversible along the top of this minor hysteresis loop (RPN_1).

It is usual to assume that the minor loop is in fact a straight line along which this reversible action takes place. The slope of such a line is known as the incremental, reversible, or recoil permeability of the material ; it varies according to the point of origin on the demagnetizing curve but between the points B_r and H_c the limits are sufficiently close to warrant the adoption of a single value for this constant.

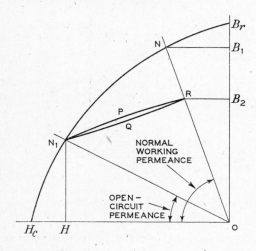

Fig.   3–8.—DEMAGNETIZA-
TION CURVE MINOR
HYSTERESIS LOOP.

Stabilizing

Deliberate depression of the working point of a permanent magnet, by subjecting it to a greater demagnetizing force than that to which it is normally subjected, is done in instances where the magnet is likely to come under the influence of additional stray fields in order that the final working flux density shall not be permanently lowered by such fields.

Due to the reversible action of a magnet working on a recoil line, the effect of the application of any field less than that represented by the H co-ordinate of the point of origin of the recoil line (OH in Fig. 3–8) is to depress temporarily the working point of flux density. On removal of this excess field the working point recovers along the recoil line to its original value.

The stabilizing effect of such intentionally applied additional demagnetizing fields is necessary in many pieces of apparatus where a high degree of constancy of magnet performance is required. A few instances are moving-coil instrument magnets, energy-meter braking magnets, and magnets for magnetron oscillators. The degree of stabilizing is usually controlled so as to give a flux drop of not less than 5 per cent. It is effected by open-circuiting the magnet by removal of its pole pieces, for generators and magnetos by the removal of the rotor, or by deliberate partial demagnetization by the application of A.C. or reversed D.C. fields. Generators are sometimes stabilized by short-circuiting the windings whilst the machine is running at speed.

A secondary advantage of stabilizing is that by selective treatment and individual measurement it is a means of providing magnets of much greater performance consistency than is normally obtained.

Efficient Utilization with Magnets on Recoil

Controlling the working point of a magnet supplying static flux with no recoil, so that it coincides with the $(BH)_{max}$ point, is a comparatively straightforward matter. With magnets working on recoil, control of leakage is important if the most efficient utilization is to be obtained. This will not necessarily be obtained

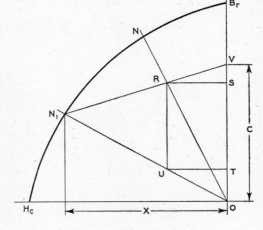

Fig. 3–9.—Working of magnet under conditions of recoil.

with a design in which this is a minimum. The useful energy developed by a magnet working at point R in Fig. 3–9 is proportional to ST × UT, and it is easily shown that this will be a maximum for the particular recoil line if the point R is midway between N_1 and V. This maximum value of recoil energy[13] is proportional to CX/4.

Recoil energy contours plotted for a series of recoil lines have the general appearance of Fig. 3–10, which is drawn for Alcomax III. Maximum recoil energy is obtained at the point marked and is realized when the leakage and working permeance lines are respectively ON_1 and ON. Any other leakage and useful permeance lines will give a useful energy of less than this value and the necessity for controlling the leakage as well as the working permeance will be obvious. Comprehensive data on recoil energies has been compiled for most of the materials shown in Tables 1, 2 and 3.[14]

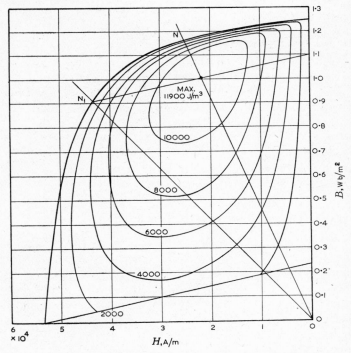

Fig. 3–10.—RECOIL ENERGY CONTOURS FOR ALCOMAX III.

Non-static Working Conditions

With many pieces of apparatus the working permeance is by no means constant.[15] In such cases the working point oscillates along a recoil line between limits set by the conditions of maximum and minimum permeance. In generators, apart from the continually changing demagnetizing effects of varying current in the armature, the reluctance of the magnetic circuit may vary according to the position of the rotor. In Fig. 3–11, as load is increased the working flux density in the magnet falls from OB_1 to OB_2.

A similar set of conditions is found with lifting magnets and magnetic chucks. In these cases open and practically closed circuit conditions may be obtained so that the working point may move along the full length of the recoil line.

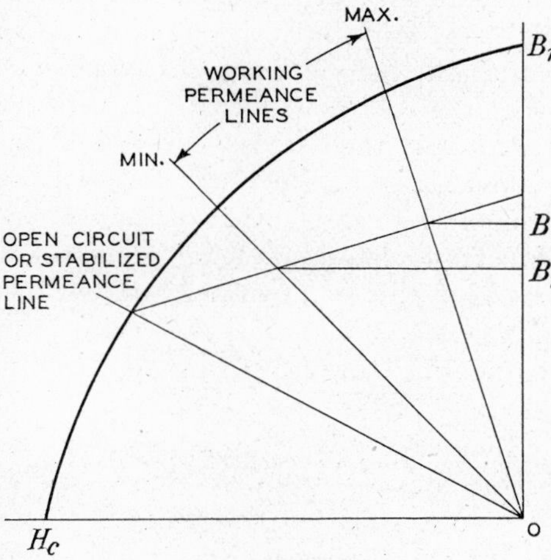

MAX.

WORKING
PERMEANCE
LINES

MIN.

B_r

Fig. 3–11.—Recoil conditions with varying working resonance.

OPEN CIRCUIT
OR STABILIZED
PERMEANCE
LINE

B_1

B_2

H_c

O

MAGNETIZING, TESTING AND DEMAGNETIZING OF PERMANENT MAGNETS

The operations of magnetizing, testing and demagnetizing permanent magnets are important to manufacturer and user alike.

The complexities of magnet manufacture are such that many makers prefer to test every magnet made in addition to the almost universal practice of sampling casts or batches. On the other hand, where large batches of a particular type are involved, quality control has certain advantages. It is equally important for the user to be able to test, as well as magnetize, his magnets in order to detect unsuitable pieces before expensive assembly operations have been carried out.

It is common practice for the user of permanent magnets to carry out his own assembly. Apart from the obvious advantages of the ease of assembly of unmagnetized pieces, serious reduction of performance is likely to result if magnetization is carried out before the magnet is assembled into its completed magnetic circuit. This last consideration of course does not arise in the comparatively few cases in which the magnet is completely finished when it leaves the manufacturer.

Magnetizing

The problem here is the provision of a field adequate to produce a flux density at least as great as the saturation density (B_s in Fig. 3–4) uniformly throughout the magnet. A very rough guide is that the magnetizing field strength should be greater than five times the coercivity of the magnet in question.

Probably the simplest form of magnetizer is the straightforward solenoid type in which bar magnets are passed through the centre. Momentary energization of the solenoid is adequate, the duration of current required being generally considerably less than one second. This short time rating means that the current loading of such solenoids can be several times that of normal electrical engineering practice, and up to 15,000 amp/sq. in. is common practice.

A more efficient type of magnetizer uses a soft-iron return circuit for the flux. As shown in Fig. 3–12 (a), the magnet is allowed to complete the flux circuit, and it is often convenient for the magnetizing gap, usually adjustable, to be external to the coil.

A modification of the solenoid type of magnetizer is shown in Fig. 3–12 (d), where a thin coil of very short axial length is used for magnetizing cobalt or tungsten steel U-shaped magnets. In order to produce a sufficient m.m.f., this type of magnetizing coil has to be very heavily stressed, and where possible magnetization of U- or arch-shaped magnets is done using the leakage field from core or pillar type magnetizers as shown in Fig. 3–12 (b). Multipole magnets are magnetized by means of an apparatus similar to that shown in Fig. 3–12 (c).

When the magnet material forms the greater part of a practi-

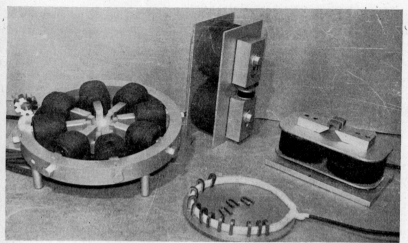

Fig. 3–12.—Various types of magnetizer.

(a) Two-pole yoke type with adjustable gap.   (b) Pillar magnetizer for " U "
magnets.   (c) Multi-pole magnetizer.   (d) Ring coil and plate for " U " magnets.

cally closed magnetic circuit and the gap is so small as to prevent
the introduction of suitable coils, a heavy-current magnetizing
method has to be used.   Unidirectional impulses of high current
at low voltage are passed through a coil of one or more turns of
heavy-section copper threaded through the aperture of the
magnet.

A D.C. magnetizing transformer is used to provide this surge
of several thousand amperes which flows in a heavy section
secondary due to the build up of primary current, or, more
commonly, to the collapse of flux in the transformer core when
the D.C. primary current is interrupted.   The ampere-turn product
produced by the single-turn magnetizing coil is adequate to give
magnetization to the saturation point if correctly designed.

The overheating of copper and the bulk of such magnetizing
transformers are a great drawback with this type of equipment,
which is being superseded to some extent by what is known as
the " ignitron magnetizer."   Essentially an A.C. equipment, the
apparatus permits the passage of several hundreds of amperes
during one half cycle of the supply frequency.   Transformation
produces currents of up to 60,000 amp in suitable magnetizing
coils.   The apparatus uses an ignitron valve connected to a

I 2

triggering circuit, the peak half-cycle heavy current passing automatically when the correct circuit conditions have been reached. Since the heavy current passes for such a short period of time, the actual power used is quite low.

Small bar magnets may be very conveniently magnetized in the gap of much larger magnets maintaining fields of 24×10^4 A/m (3,000 oersteds) or more.

Testing

The B.S.I. Panel. This equipment affords a means of obtaining the demagnetization characteristics of permanent magnets or of control test pieces quite accurately and quickly. It is suitable for testing on one axis only and pieces should have a direction of magnetization which is more or less straight ; except where the test is being used for comparison only, the section must be uniform throughout the length. The ends of magnets to be tested using this equipment must be ground flat and parallel.

The apparatus consists essentially of a Faraday homopolar generator, the magnetic field for which is supplied by the magnet

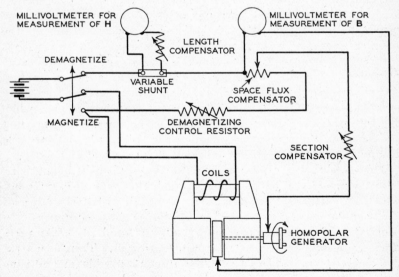

Fig. 3–13.—THEORETICAL DIAGRAM OF B.S.I. TESTING EQUIPMENT 406 : 1931.

Fig. 3–14.—B.S.I. TESTING APPARATUS 406.

under test, and a series of instruments, switches and resistors for measuring and controlling the generator output and the current used in the magnetizing coil.

A connection diagram is shown in Fig. 3–13, and the arrangement of the instrument panel and generator is shown in Fig. 3–14.

Flux from the magnet passes through the Permalloy pole pieces and disc of the generator. Driven at constant speed by the motor, the disc will have generated in it between its centre and periphery an e.m.f. proportional to the flux crossing it. This e.m.f. is divided by means of a resistance network known as the section compensator in such a way that only a fraction of it is measured by a sensitive millivoltmeter (shown as a *B*-meter). The resistance network is so calibrated that this fraction is inversely proportional to the section of the sample, and in consequence this millivoltmeter can be calibrated to indicate flux density directly.

The magnetizing or demagnetizing field is controlled by the

magnetizing switch and control resistances, the demagnetizing field $-H$ being measured by a second millivoltmeter. A second resistance network—the length compensator, which is similar to that used with the B-meter—enables this instrument to be calibrated directly in units of H.

Other devices of the apparatus include a shunt selector switch to extend the range of the H-meter and a potentiometer permitting compensation for field flux crossing the disc but not passing through the magnet. The apparatus at the present time is manufactured and calibrated only for C.G.S. units and measures directly only the $4\pi J/H$ curve. Correction to the true B/H curve is easy, and the reader is referred to the specification for this instrument, which gives a full explanation of other corrections to be made to give the most accurate results.[16]

The Fluxmeter. Probably the most widely used instrument for magnet testing, particularly where large numbers are involved, is the fluxmeter. Used in conjunction with suitable easily-made search coils, it affords a most accurate means of measuring fluxes, at a point or over an area within an air space, or within the section of part of a magnet. It is essentially for testing finished magnets where the conditions of demagnetization are the self-demagnetizing ones and is a means of measuring fluxes equal or proportional to some point on or within the demagnetization curve.

It is similar to a moving-coil galvanometer except that it has negligible restoring torque, the angular movement of its pointer or scale being proportional to the flux linkage change produced in a search coil connected to it. Usual calibration constants are 3,000, 5,000 and 10,000 maxwell-turns per division, corresponding to 3×10^{-5}, 5×10^{-5} and 10×10^{-5} weber-turns, the normal scale length being 120 divisions with the pointer type and 240 divisions with a projected scale version.

Calculations of flux or flux change are made, using the simple formulæ

$$\text{Flux} = \frac{\text{Deflection} \times \text{Scale constant}}{\text{No. of search-coil turns}}$$

$$\text{Flux Density } B = \frac{\text{Deflection} \times \text{Scale constant}}{\text{No. of search-coil turns} \times \text{Mean search-coil area.}}$$

The Gaussmeter. This instrument is convenient for measuring field strengths at a point since it gives a steady deflection and does not depend upon relative motion.

A probe element consisting of a moving-coil carrying constant current is inserted into the field at the point at which measurement is required. The moving-coil rotates against the restoring torque of hair springs and a pointer indicates the deflection which is proportional to the flux density at the point. Alternatively, the moving-coil is replaced by a small permanent magnet, also controlled by hair springs. Rotation to the point of maximum deflection is necessary.

The Ballistic Galvanometer. Testing methods using the ballistic galvanometer are usually confined to laboratory work in the accurate determination of hysteresis loops or, more particularly, demagnetization curves. The most accurate results are obtained on ring specimens, but these are inconvenient to use and, with modern high-coercivity alloys, only small errors are introduced by using rectilinear or cylindrical test pieces with a high-permeability yoke or pole-piece arrangement. It is usual to wind the search coil for the measurement of flux density onto the test piece and to use an accurately fitting magnetizing coil over this. Field or H determinations may be made by a direct computation from the product of current and magnetizing coil turns or alternatively by measurement using H-coils clamped onto the sample. These H coils may be of the flat type or the semi-circular Chattock potentiometer type, and must be individually calibrated. All pole-piece joints should be ground flat and smooth to cut down the yoke reluctance.

The circuit used is the basic one for magnetic measurements, and is shown in Fig. 3–15. Calibration is usually effected by a mutual inductance method, and points on the hysteresis loop

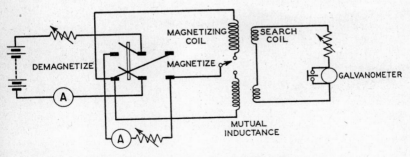

Fig. 3–15.—BALLISTIC GALVANOMETER CIRCUTTAY.

are obtained by the step-by-step method given in most text-books on electrotechnology.

Occasionally the ballistic galvanometer is used for production testing of permanent magnets where extreme accuracy is required. The flux-linkage changes necessary to produce galvanometer deflections and thus to permit measurement are usually obtained by the use of search coils as with fluxmeter testing.

Special-purpose Tests

The most important criterion of a magnet's usefulness is the performance which it maintains in its final design, or in conjunction with its associated equipment. Where possible production testing is designed to simulate the final working conditions as nearly as possible. This is comparatively simple in the case of such magnets as those for loudspeakers, instruments and cathode ray tube focusing, but is not practicable for magnets for generators, motors and magnetos. For these magnets it is usual to arrange an arbitrary test to reproduce the final conditions of demagnetization as nearly as possible and to measure the flux produced by the magnet under these conditions. A quite common method is

Fig. 3–16.—APPARATUS FOR TESTING MAGNETS UNDER CONTROLLED CONDITIONS OF DEMAGNETIZATION.

Testing is effected by withdrawing the small block magnet, shown on the magnetizer base, from a small soft iron yoke housed between the magnetizer pole pieces. This yoke is wound with search coils and the demagnetizing is controlled by the length of air-gap between the ends of the magnet and the yoke poles.

to measure the flux change in a small iron yoke on removal of the magnet. The necessary demagnetization is controlled by adjustment of the air-gaps in the yoke or by applying a definite fixed demagnetizing current to a suitable winding. It is convenient to house such a device within the actual magnetizer—as shown in Fig. 3–16.

Demagnetizing

Demagnetizing of permanent magnets is necessary many times during production in order to facilitate handling during finishing operations. It is most commonly done by means of a solenoid carrying alternating current at mains frequency. Provided that the maximum field at the solenoid centre is sufficient to effect the reversible magnetization of the magnet to saturation point, the gradual weakening of the field on withdrawal of the magnet leaves it in a sufficiently demagnetized state. Alternatively, with the magnet at the solenoid centre the current may be gradually reduced to zero.

The excessive loadings necessitated by modern high-coercivity alloys can be dissipated by water circulation in a low-voltage high-current coil made of copper tubing. This method is advantageous where quantities of large magnets are involved.

When the magnet has a practically closed circuit, or when its assembly is such that it is surrounded by a conducting metal, for instance a die-casting, the demagnetization possible by the above methods may be inadequate. This is because of the closed circuit in the one instance and because of the shielding effect of eddy currents induced in the conducting metal, in the other. For such magnets demagnetization must be done on the equipment normally used for magnetizing, the direction of current being continually reversed and gradually reduced to zero.

THE HANDLING AND STORAGE OF MAGNETS

For a variety of reasons probably 95 per cent. of all permanent magnets are supplied in an unmagnetized state. Where subsequent assembly has to be carried out, as for instance the assembly of magnets in a flywheel magneto, unmagnetized pieces are easier to handle. Furthermore, open-circuiting may seriously reduce the performance, as is explained under " Permanent Magnet Design."

A further point is the difficulty of packing magnetized magnets so that one will not demagnetize another.

Handling of Unmagnetized Magnets

The safe handling of unmagnetized permanent magnets is no more difficult than the handling of other steel parts so long as the inherent brittleness of so many of these special highly alloyed materials is remembered. The damage which can occur to magnetized magnets is particularly serious, however, in that there is no apparent effect and the damage may not be detected until the equipment is in the final stages of production and test. Careful precautions are necessary therefore to circumvent the possibility of magnetic damage in all operations of manufacture subsequent to magnetization.

Demagnetization and Flux Distortion

Magnetic spoiling may take the form of direct demagnetization or of flux distortion at the pole faces. The former may happen due to the presence of opposing magnetic fields of other magnets (i.e. when they are in repulsion) and occurs to a limited extent if any part of a magnet is short-circuited by some iron or steel body. The effect of open-circuiting or of removing a magnet from its pole pieces constitutes a direct demagnetization. Stray fields from electrical equipment may be sufficient to cause a permanent flux reduction.

Where stabilized magnets are concerned, it will be appreciated that permanent harm from any of the above effects will only result if they are in excess of the stabilizing field.

Pole-flux Distortion

Pole-flux distortion can occur when two magnetized magnets which are in attraction are separated by sliding motion. It also happens to a limited extent when magnets are slid from a keeper or set of pole pieces. The effect in either case is a cross-magnetizing of the magnet in the immediate vicinity of the pole tips and a permanent distortion of the magnet flux when the motion is completed. Magnets should therefore be separated by a direct pull or where this is not possible by a lever and hingeing motion.

The reduction in performance due to any of these effects is instantaneous and is recoverable only by remagnetizing. The seriousness will be obvious with magnets which have been stabilized or which have had their flux adjusted within close limits, as is the practice with some instrument magnets and with those for radar.

Prevention of any of the above demagnetizing effects is quite easy and it will be obvious that the most important factor is the adequate separation of magnetized magnets. If the design is such that the leakage field is great, a separation of 1 in. or more is necessary, and because of the attraction between magnets, this is best obtained by the use of non-magnetic trays or boxes. When the leakage field is low, as is often so when the air-gap length is small, a spacing less than this is sufficient and cardboard or paper wrappings may be adequate. Experience is the best guide, and one should err on the side of safety by having as great a spacing as is practicable.

Non-magnetic Tools

Non-magnetic tools and gauges should always be used with magnetized magnets.

MAGNET APPLICATIONS

Electricity Meter Magnets

Large numbers of magnets for electricity meters are manufactured in tungsten, chromium and the lower grades of cobalt steels, proved designs having remained unchanged in some cases for many years. Long-term stability is of paramount importance with magnets for electricity meters, and since this can only be proved after a long time interval, the reluctance of manufacturers to change is understandable. However, the increased coercivities and consequent greater resistance to demagnetization of newer alloys make them particularly suitable for applications such as electricity meters ; and, furthermore, they are not susceptible to shift of characteristics due to the gradual precipitation of carbides as are the older steels. Consequently more and more meter manufacturers are re-designing their meters to use the newer diffusion-hardening alloys.

The very greatly reduced length/section ratio of optimum-efficiency magnets in these alloys has necessitated a complete readjustment of ideas regarding braking-magnet design.

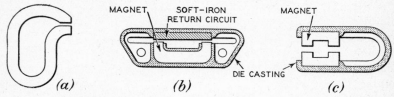

Fig. 3–17.—ELECTRICITY METER BRAKING MAGNET SYSTEM.

Fig. 3–17 (a) shows the general type of magnet made in the older steels. The difficulties of providing a sufficient clearance for the meter disc when an anisotropic magnet is used is overcome either by fixing a magnet in a suitable frame and providing a soft-iron return path for the flux or by using two smaller magnets having a common flux path as shown respectively by Figs. 3–17 (b) and 3–17 (c).

Instrument Magnets

A conventional form of moving-coil instrument magnet suitable for manufacture in any grade of magnet steel up to 35 per cent. cobalt is shown in Fig. 3–18 (a). The increased efficiency of modern alloys is taken advantage of by designs using block or arch-shaped magnets in Alnico, Alcomax or Ticonal fitted to soft-iron pole pieces as shown in Figs. 3–18 (b) and 3–18 (c). The provision of the many small tapped and drilled holes often required for mounting the movement is simplified with these forms of assembly since the pole pieces are soft iron.

Methods of fastening such block magnets are by clamping through a central hole or, preferably, a slot, by soldering or brazing, or when unit construction of the pole piece assembly is use, by magnetic attraction only.

The high coercive force and working flux densities of the anisotropic alloys make the form of instrument magnet shown in Fig. 3–18 (d) possible. All the magnet material is contained within the cylindrical centre pole, which is magnetized along a diameter. With normal air-gap lengths flux densities with this type of design seldom exceed 0·2 Wb/m.² (2,000 gauss).

Generator, Motor and Magneto Magnets

Although many efficient machines are still made using 15 and 35 per cent. cobalt steels, the trend with this type of machine is

towards the use of the higher-performance alloys. The higher
energies available enable ever-increasing performance demands
to be met, and because of the reduction in magnet size the whole
machine can be scaled down. Another great advantage found
with the newer alloys is their greatly increased stability at high
temperatures. It is not uncommon for such machines to work at
temperatures approaching 100° C. At such temperatures the
gradual dispersion of carbides in the cobalt steels, or ageing, as it
is called, is accelerated. If this is not allowed for in design the
performance of the machine may suffer. All the aluminium-

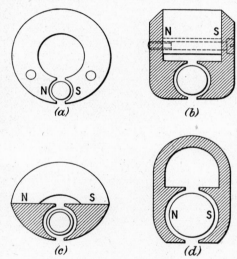

Fig. 3–18.—MOVING COIL IN-
STRUMENT MAGNET SYSTEMS.
(*a*) Magnet steel up to 35 per
cent. cobalt.
(*b*) and (*c*) Block or arch-
shaped magnets fitted to soft-
iron pole-pieces.
(*d*) Cylindrical centre pole
magnetized along a diameter.

nickel-cobalt steels are completely stable at temperatures
considerably in excess of this.[14]
 Various designs for magnet assemblies for such machines are
shown in Figs. 3–20 to 3–24. A conventional design is illustrated
in Fig. 3–20 (*a*). In this the magnets are stationary and are often
simple rectilinear blocks. No difficulties of fixing arise since it is
usual to fasten the laminated pole pieces into the machine casing
and fix the magnet by simple clamping. Typical rotor magnet
assemblies are shown in Figs. 3–20 (*b*) and 3–21 : in Fig. 3–20 (*b*)
a die-casting is formed around the magnets and pole pieces and
sometimes also the machine spindle. Fig. 3–21 shows a method
of producing a multiple rotor with a two-pole magnet.

Fig. 3–19.—Various types of electricity meter brake magnets and moving-coil instrument magnets.

The instrument magnet in the centre of the front row is an example of brazed construction and consists of an arch-shaped Alcomax magnet block with mild steel pole pieces.

Magnetized axially, the magnet supplies flux to soft iron or laminated fingers which project and are interlaced, so producing the desired alternate polarity around the rotor periphery. This method of assembly is particularly useful when it is required to use an anisotropic alloy, since it simplifies the heat treatment magnetization.

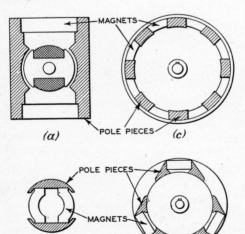

Fig. 3–20.—Various magneto and generator magnet and pole piece arrangements.

(a) Conventional design.
(b) Rotor magnet assembly.
(c) and (d) Flywheel-type rotors.

Fig. 3–21.—A B.T.H. MAGNETO.

The eight poles of the rotor of this magneto are obtained by using " fingered " pole pieces in conjunction with a two-pole cylindrical magnet which is magnetized axially.

A rotor magnet can sometimes be cast directly onto its shaft or onto a soft iron sleeve which, during the casting process, is incorporated in the sand mould, the shaft being suitably keyed to prevent rotation and axial movement of the magnet. Final

Fig. 3–22.—EXAMPLES OF GOOD MODERN MAGNETO AND GENE-RATOR ROTOR DE-SIGNS.

Simple magnet shapes in an isotropic or anisotropic alloy are fitted with laminated pole pieces and are securely assembled together with spindle or bushing in a pressure die casting. Final machining is carried out after the casting operation.

(*Industrial Magneto Co. Ltd.*)

Fig. 3–23.—A SELECTION OF MAGNETO, GENERATOR, AND MOTOR MAGNETS.

machining of shaft and magnet must be carried out after heat treatment. The method is generally only suitable for two-pole rotors in anisotropic alloys ; where a greater number of poles is required, one of the isotropic alloys is usually used.

The flywheel-type of rotor is used on many magnetos, and magneto alternators have usually six or more poles—typical forms of construction are shown in Figs. 3–20 (c) and 3–20 (d). In Fig. 3–20 (c) segmental magnets and lamination blocks are pressed or moulded into a suitable wheel. Only half the number of magnets is used in the type shown in Fig. 3–20 (d), in which

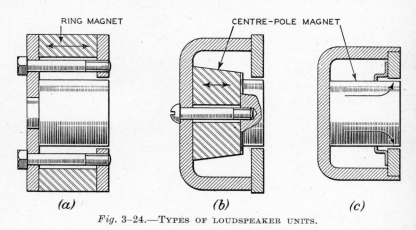

Fig. 3–24.—TYPES OF LOUDSPEAKER UNITS.

the manufacture is simplified by using rectilinear blocks. Magnets and laminations are moulded into a die-casting.

Magnets for Radio

The improved performances achieved by the use of anisotropic alloys and the reduction in size and scaling down of other parts which this has made possible have led to their almost universal adoption for magnets for loudspeakers, microphones and for the focusing of television tubes.

All modern loudspeakers are of the moving-coil type, which have a diaphragm to which is attached a light coil arranged to move freely in the annular air-gap of the magnet, usually a permanent one. Magnets are generally of one of the types shown in section in Fig. 3–24.

The first of these uses a ring of magnet alloy magnetized axially, clamped between mild-steel pole pieces as shown. The efficiency reckoned as the ratio of flux in the gap to total magnet flux is about 40 per cent., falling as the gap field exceeds 1 Wb/m.^{2} (10,000 gauss).

The slug or central-pole type is shown in Fig. 3–24 (b) and comprises a magnet block surmounted by a cylindrical soft-iron

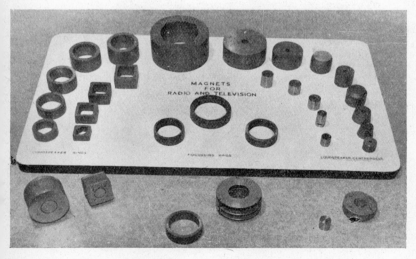

Fig. 3–25.—VARIOUS MAGNETS FOR RADIO. COMPLETE ASSEMBLIES ARE SHOWN IN THE FOREGROUND.

LOUD SPEAKERS USING
RING-TYPE MAGNETS.

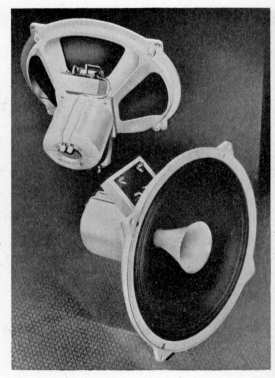

Fig. 3–26.—THESE ILLUS-
TRATIONS SHOW LOUD-
SPEAKERS USING RING-
TYPE MAGNETS.

The two loudspeakers
shown on the right are of
the duplex type. They
have a conventional voice
coil and diaphragm at the
front of the magnet and a
secondary coil for high-
frequency response at the
rear. This coil loads the
central cone through a
hole in the centre pole of
the magnet assembly.

(*Whiteley Electrical Radio
Co. Ltd.*)

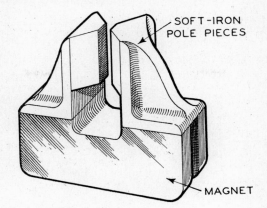

SOFT-IRON
POLE PIECES

Fig. 3–27.—TYPICAL RIBBON-
MICROPHONE ASSEMBLY.

MAGNET

tip, the whole being fixed into a cup or yoke with a front plate to form the outer gap face and return circuit for the flux : the maximum efficiency is around 55 per cent. A modification of this type, Fig. 3–24 (c), uses a centre pole made completely of magnetic alloy. Efficiencies as high as 65 per cent. are obtained within a very limited range of gap flux density, using Alcomax or Ticonal, which is directionally magnetized so that the flux lines, normal to

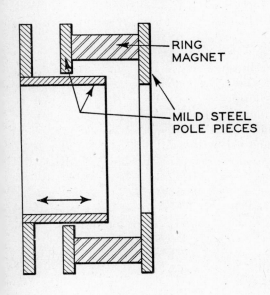

RING
MAGNET

MILD STEEL
POLE PIECES

Fig. 3–28.—THIS ILLUSTRA-
TION SHOWS THE GENERAL
FOCUSING MAGNET ASSEM-
BLY.

Fig. 3–29.—MAGNETS USED IN RADAR EQUIPMENT.

the axis throughout the greater part of the centre pole, are turned through 90° in the vicinity of the air-gap. These last two types are widely used in television receivers, for which they are particularly suitable, owing to their almost complete lack of external leakage field due to the shielding effect of the soft-iron cup or yoke.

Various assembly methods are used ; ring types are invariably clamped with screws as shown ; centre poles may be screwed, soldered, brazed or held solely by magnetic attraction. In this latter case a positioning device for centralizing the centre pole is necessary. Microphone magnets of the moving-coil type utilize a magnet essentially similar to that of a loudspeaker. Ribbon types use magnets similar to those shown in Fig. 3–27.

Focusing magnets for cathode-ray tubes use magnets basically of the form shown in Fig. 3–28. Flux densities at the centre of the annulus of the order of 0·02–0·03 Wb/m.² (200–300 gauss) are usual. Magnets of short length are required because of space considerations, and since they usually work on almost open magnetic circuits, and consequently have a low permeance, the alloys having very high coercivity such as Alcomax III, IV or Hycomax are most suitable.

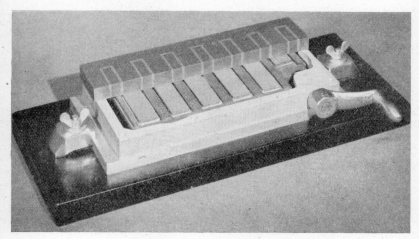

Fig. 3-30.—A MAGNETIC CHUCK.

The work plate is cut away to show the magnet assembly. Blocks of Alcomax are cast into a movable cast-steel yoke arranged to slide under the work plates by means of a lever. It is shown in the " on " position. Movement to the left causes short-circuiting of the magnets and reduction of the field emanating from the surface of the work plate.

Fig. 3-31.—A MAGNETIC SHEET FLOATER.

An interesting application of permanent magnets. Suitably housed " U " magnets magnetize steel sheets placed between them. The induced polarities are such that like poles are opposed, and the sheets repel one another, the top sheet floating quite clear of the others leading to easy handling.

(*James Neill & Co. (Sheffield) Ltd.*)

Radar Magnets

The very high performances required of magnets for use with magnetron oscillators are achieved only by accurate design. This is outside the scope of this book, and Fig. 3–29 is included merely to show the types of magnet in use. The methods of construction are obvious. In the type having two horn-shaped magnet blocks with a soft iron base, attachment is by means of screws passing through this base into holes tapped into soft-iron cores which are moulded into the magnets during casting ; such inserts are grooved and knurled to prevent movement, and the method is suitable only where the mass of the magnet is great compared with the insert.

Only magnet materials of the highest internal energy are capable of producing the performances required within the permissible limits of weight.

Fig. 3–30 shows a magnetic chuck, with the work plate cut away to reveal the magnet assembly. An interesting application of permanent magnetization is shown in Fig. 3–31. Steel sheets are magnetized by being placed between " U " magnets, the induced polarities being such that like poles are opposed. The magnetized sheets will thus repel one another and facilitate easier handling.

Acknowledgments

The author wishes to record his appreciation of the facilities afforded by the directors of Marrison and Catherall Ltd., for taking the various magnet and equipment photographs and for permission to publish much of the technical data given in the various tables. The standard demagnetization and recoil characteristics are reproduced by courtesy of the Permanent Magnet Association. Thanks are also due to the various firms which have given permission for specialized magnet designs to be included in the various figures and illustrations, in particular : Ferranti Ltd., and Officine Galileo (Florence) for energy meter magnet designs ; Industrial Magneto Co. Ltd. and the British Thomson Houston Co. Ltd., for magneto magnet designs ; Whiteley Electrical Radio Co. Ltd., for loudspeaker illustrations ; and James Neill & Co. (Sheffield) Ltd., for the photographs of a magnetic chuck and sheet floater.

References

1. HONDA, K., and SAITO, S. " KS Magnetic Steels," *Phys. Rev.*, 1920, **16**, 494.
2. MISHIMA, T. " Nickel Aluminium Steel for Permanent Magnets," *Ohm*, 1932, **19**.
3. HORSBURGH, G. D. L., and TETLEY, F. W. British Patent Spec. Nos. 431660 and 439543.
4. OLIVER, D. A., and SHEDDEN, J. W. " Cooling of Permanent Magnet Alloys in a Constant Magnetic Field," *Nature*, 1938, **142**, 209.
5. PHILIPS, N. V., GLOEILAMPENFABRIEKEN. British Patent Spec. No. 522731 (1938).
6. EDWARDS, A. British Patent Spec. No. 577135 (1940).
7. PERMANENT MAGNET ASSOCIATION. " An Improved Permanent Magnet Material," *Jour. of Scientific Instruments*, 1945, **22**, 56.
8. TYRELL, A. J. " The Design and Application of Modern Permanent Magnets," *Jour. B.I.R.E.*, 1946, Sept.
9. TETLEY, F. W. British Patent Spec. 583411 (1946).
10. HADFIELD, D. British Patent Spec. 634686 (1950).
11. HADFIELD, D. British Patent Spec. 634700 (1950).
12. GARVIN, S. J. " The Production of Sintered Permanent Magnets," *Iron & Steel Inst. Special Report*, No. 38 (1947).
13. EDWARDS, A., and HOSELITZ, K. " Permanent Magnet Design," *Elect. Rev.*, Aug. 4th, 1944.
14. PERMANENT MAGNET ASSOCIATION. Brochure 1952.
15. DESMOND, D. J. " The Economic Utilization of Modern Permanent Magnets," *Jour. I.E.E.*, 1945, **92**, Part II, 229.
16. BRITISH STANDARDS INSTITUTION. Spec. 406. 1931. " Apparatus for Workshop Testing of Permanent Magnets."

3. (b) MICROPOWDER MAGNETS

PERMANENT magnets made from soft ferro-magnetic metal powders are now being manufactured in this country after some years of development work. They are moulded by high-pressure methods from extremely fine powders of iron or iron-alloys, known as micropowders, which derive their permanent-magnet properties solely from the fineness of their particle or crystal size.

Coercive Force and Particle Size

From the domain theory, Néel during the last war deduced that very fine particles of iron of the order of magnitude of a magnetic domain would exhibit very high coercive force exceeding any value hitherto obtained in conventional magnets. The required optimum particle size was about one-hundredth that of the finest powder hitherto made for radio cores, but the preparation, even on a small scale, was difficult and hazardous because such powder has an extremely strong affinity for oxygen and spontaneously oxidizes when exposed to the air. The magnetic quality of this highly pyrophoric powder could be maintained only by immersing the micropowder in inflammable liquids such as benzine which tended to increase the hazard.

It was found experimentally that coercive forces approaching 80,000 A/m (1,000 oersteds) could be obtained from pure iron reduced in dry hydrogen from ferrous formate and the best results were obtained with a particle of crystal size of 0·01 to 0·1 micron (1 micron = 0·001 mm or 10,000 Angstrom units). Below this critical size range, the coercive force is rapidly reduced to figures inadequate for permanent magnets. Theoretically, the maximum coercive force of pure iron approaches 800,000 A/m (10,000 oersteds) but this assumes that the particles are elongated and of optimum dimensions oriented in one required direction.

These figures with the appropriate particle-size range are shown diagrammatically in Fig. 3–32, which indicates approximate values of coercive force plotted on a logarithmic scale. This diagram shows how the same raw material, pure iron in powder form, can give two grades of magnetic material with opposite performance. The coarse range above 1 micron is of practical

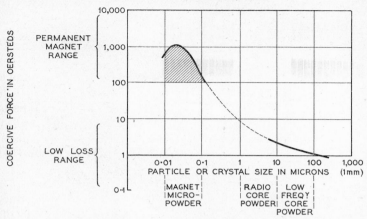

Fig. 3–32.—RELATION BETWEEN COERCIVE FORCE AND PARTICLE SIZE OF PURE IRON IN POWDER FORM.

Between 0·01 and 0·1 microns, particle size is suitable for pressing into permanent magnets, while for coarser powders the coercive force falls to values associated with low-loss cores.

value on account of its low loss and the micropowder range below 0·1 micron gives useful permanent-magnet properties.

The best performance is obtained by making magnets from an iron-alloy micropowder containing 30 per cent. cobalt but, on account of the high price of this metal, cheaper grades are made with lower percentages of cobalt or from pure iron prepared from less expensive raw materials.

Commercially-available Micropowder Magnets

Permanent magnets are made from micropowders by high-pressure moulding. When compressed, the physical density and the magnetic flux density, which are closely related, increase progressively at the expense of the coercive force. In this way a large variety of B/H curves can be obtained.

The considerable difficulties associated with the low density and highly-pyrophoric nature of the micropowders have now been overcome on a production scale with new techniques.

Conventional demagnetization curves for two qualities of Gecalloy micropowder magnet are given in Fig. 3—33, the code letters being H for high quality (alloy) and M for medium quality (iron). Each is available in two grades to meet different design conditions, the letters R and C representing respectively the high-

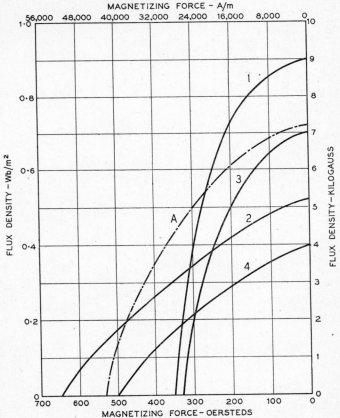

Fig. 3–33.—BH CURVES (MINIMUM) FOR GECALLOY MICROPOWDER MAGNETS.
Curve 1—HR.   High-quality (alloy), high remanence.   Energy factor, 1·5.
Curve 2—HC.   High-quality (alloy), high coercive.   Energy factor, 1·1.
Curve 3—MR.   Medium quality (iron), high remanence.   Energy factor, 1·0.
Curve 4—MC.   Medium quality (iron), high coercive.   Energy factor, 0·6.
Curve A—Best non-oriented cast magnet, for comparison.
    (Energy factors (BH_{max}) expressed in mega-gauss-oersted.)
                                        (Salford Electrical Instruments Ltd.)

remanence and high-coercivity grades.   A closed or partly-closed
magnetic circuit requires a comparatively low coercive force to
maintain the flux and thus a magnet with higher remanence can
be used (Types HR or MR).   An open magnetic circuit requires
a higher coercive force which results in lower remanence (Types
HC and MC) ; hence a larger section of magnet is necessary to
carry the same flux as in the earlier case.

Comparison with Cast-alloy and Steel Magnets

The high-quality micropowder magnets have an energy factor equivalent to that of the best non-oriented (isotropic) cast-alloy magnets. At the present stage of development, micropowder magnets are not available with the greater energy factors of the highly-directional (anisotropic) cast magnets. However, since micropowder magnets are nearly half the weight of cast magnets of the same size, the difference in performance is comparatively small and can be often neutralized by the improved designs which the new magnets make possible.

The medium-quality micropowder magnets have rather better magnetic properties than the whole range of tungsten, chrome and cobalt steels, especially regarding coercive force which is the principal magnetic factor affecting stability. These micro-powder magnets are made from pure iron produced with materials obtained in this country and effect a saving in imported metals.

Physical Properties

Possibly the chief advantage of micropowder magnets consists of the much lower physical density in comparison with other types. For the high-remanence magnets the density is about 5 g/cm^3., but for the high-coercive force types it is in the region of 4 g/cm^3. The latter are usually made with a plastic binder to maintain mechanical strength and this increases the specific resistance to that of an insulator and opens up possibilities of use under A.C. conditions. High-remanence types are made without binders and are thus of low electrical resistivity.

Due to the softness of micropowders, it is possible to mould them into magnets to accurate dimensions without final grinding. The production methods for micropowder magnets are limited throughout to low temperatures and so it is possible to include shafts, pole pieces, or inserts of various other metals into the mouldings.

For small quantities and samples, micropowder magnets and magnet systems are made by shaping and grinding pressed compacts to the required design.

By moulding complete magnetic systems with pole pieces and inserts and by using the special shapes that moulding makes possible, a great improvement in the design of electro-magnetic components and equipment can be achieved.

4. PERMANENT MAGNET FERRITES

By

B. W. St. Leger Montague, B.Sc.

The earliest-known substance to exhibit permanent magnetic properties was the lodestone or natural ore of magnetite (Fe_3O_4). It can be regarded as the forerunner of the modern ferrite permanent magnet. The extension of this class of magnetic materials has been very recent : it is only since 1945 that appreciable development has taken place.

Early Work

In 1925 G. Aminoff observed that a mineral containing lead and iron oxides was strongly attracted by a magnet and suggested for it the name " magnetoplumbite." V. Adelsköld, in 1938, determined from X-ray measurements that the crystal structure of magnetoplumbite is hexagonal, and proposed the chemical formula $PbO.6Fe_2O_3$; he also found that the compounds $BaO.6Fe_2O_3$ and $SrO.6Fe_2O_3$ have a similar crystal structure. Other workers have found that $BaO.6Fe_2O_3$ contains a ferromagnetic phase.

Early Japanese work on cobalt ferrites as permanent magnets was described in 1933 and 1940. A recent British patent describes a method of manufacture of cobalt ferrite magnets yielding a better material.

The most recent work on permanent magnet ferrites of the magnetoplumbite group has been described by Went, et al. (1952). A general survey is given by Brockman (1952).

Properties of Ferrite Permanent Magnets

The magnetically " hard " ferrites are characterized chiefly by their high coercive force, somewhat low remanent induction, and an appreciably lower value of $(BH)_{max}$ compared with the more conventional metal magnets. They are magnetically very stable and difficult to demagnetize, either by external magnetic fields or by mechanical shock. They usually possess a negative temperature-coefficient of remanence which may be of the order of 0·2 per cent. per deg. C., some ten times greater than that of a metal alloy magnet, and although this is often a disadvantage, it can, on occasion, be put to practical use.

The combination of large coercivity and relatively low remanence gives rise to demagnetization curves of the form shown in Fig. 4–1, which also gives comparative curves of a high-grade metal magnet. It can be seen that for the ferrite magnet (a) there is a large difference between the two points $_BH_C$ and $_JH_C$, which are, respectively, the values of the field H at which the induction B and magnetization J are reduced to zero, whereas for the metal magnet (b) the two points are almost coincident. The practical

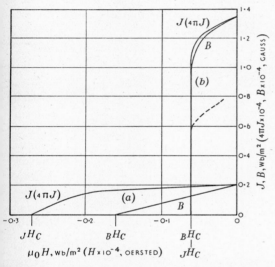

Fig. 4–1.—DEMAGNETIZATION CURVES PRODUCED FROM COMBINATION OF LARGE COERCIVITY AND RELATIVELY LOW REMANENCE FOR FERRITE MAGNET (a) AND COMPARATIVE CURVES OF A HIGH-GRADE METAL MAGNET (b).

implications of this will be discussed later. It may be noted here that the ferrite magnets are resistant to demagnetization by heating, provided the Curie temperature is not approached too closely. For the barium ferrite, the Curie point is at about 450° C.

The electrical resistivity of these materials is very large, frequently exceeding 10^6 ohm-m (10^8 ohm-cm). This can be of value in applications where a permanent magnet is required to polarize the core of an inductor or transformer carrying alternating fields, for eddy-current losses in a ferrite magnet are usually negligible.

The most recent developments in ferrite permanent magnets have been described by Went, Rathenau, Gorter and van Oosterhout (1952). They discuss in considerable detail the properties and crystal structure of ferrites in the magneto-plumbite group having the formula $MO.6Fe_2O_3$, where M represents one of the metals Ba, Pb or Sr. For commercial reasons the barium compound, which may be written $BaFe_{12}O_{19}$, is generally preferred, and is marketed in Britain and the U.S.A. under the name " Magnadur." Since much more work appears to have been published on the structure of the magnetoplumbites than on that of the cobalt ferrites, we shall discuss the theory of permanent magnet ferrites on the basis of the former group, though there is reason to believe that the two classes of material have much in common.

Composition and Manufacture

The ferrites used for permanent magnets consist of mixed oxides of iron and one or more other metals, the heat treatment of the mixed oxides producing complex crystals with the required magnetic properties. Early work on these materials seems to have been devoted almost entirely to mixtures of iron and cobalt oxides, and although these cobalt ferrites are apparently still being investigated, there is little published information on their properties and even less on their structure.

A cobalt ferrite material is marketed in the U.S.A. under the name of " Vectolite." It is prepared from a mixture of iron and cobalt oxides. This is pressed and sintered at about 1,000° C. and allowed to cool to 300° C., when a magnetic field is applied in the required direction and the subsequent cooling to room temperature takes place in the field. This magnetic treatment makes the material anisotropic, and increases the $(BH)_{max}$ obtainable to about 4,000 J/m^3 (0·5 m.g.o.). The remanence B_r is 0·16 Wb/m^2 (1,600 gauss), and the coercive force $_BH_C$ is about 70,000 $A/metre$ (900 oersteds).

Cobalt ferrite magnets are described in British Patent Specifications Nos. 594,474 and 596,875. The values claimed for coercive force and remanence are somewhat higher than the figures above, apparently due to the special methods of preparation.

The method of manufacture of barium ferrites is in principle similar to that for cobalt ferrites, but many variations are possible.

From the point of view of mechanical properties, ferrite magnets vary considerably, according to their particular method of manufacture. Since they are made from finely divided oxides mixed with a binding agent, compressed and baked, the mechanical properties depend to a large extent upon the nature of the binder, the amount of compression and the subsequent heat treatment. In general, however, the ferrites are hard and brittle and are frequently classed as ceramics. They are often harder than glass and until recently could be machined only by grinding or cutting with a diamond wheel.*

Moulding under pressure a very finely divided mixture leads to a product extremely compact and free from cavities and inclusions. Thus, ferrite magnets being very homogenous, can be used without polepieces and yokes where this would be an advantage.

Theory of Permanent Magnet Ferrites

In discussing the current theories underlying the behaviour of this class of permanent magnet we shall consider separately the coercive force and the remanence of the materials. When necessary we shall distinguish between the B-coercive force $_BH_C$ and the J-coercive force $_JH_C$.

There are three main factors which contribute to the coercive force of a magnetic material : (a) the magnetic anisotropy of the crystal ; (b) the stress anisotropy ; and (c) the shape anisotropy. In the case of the oxides M $Fe_{12}O_{19}$, where M represents one of the elements Ba, Pb or Sr, the crystal anisotropy appears to play a dominant part in determining the coercive force. The stress anisotropy is also considered to be of some importance, but owing to the difficulty of estimating the internal stresses the contribution of the stress anisotropy to the coercive force is not yet clear.

Compared with the crystal anisotropy the shape anisotropy is small, due to the low saturation magnetization of these oxide materials. In any case, it is found that the behaviour of $BaFe_{12}O_{19}$ can be explained fairly satisfactorily by considering only the crystal anisotropy. It can be shown (Stoner and Wohlfarth, 1948) that for a single crystal of $BaFe_{12}O_{19}$, which has one preferential

* Neppiras (1953) has developed a new method of cutting and drilling such hard materials by means of an ultra-sonically-driven tool.

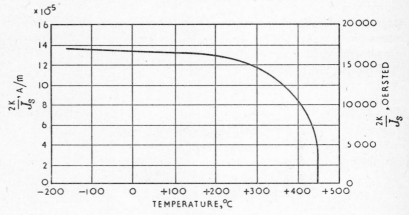

Fig. 4–2.—THE CURVE OF $2K/J_s$ AGAINST TEMPERATURE.

direction of magnetization along the hexagonal axis, the field strength necessary to reverse the magnetization direction against the crystal anisotropy is approximately $2K/J_s$, where K is the first anisotropy coefficient and J_s is the saturation magnetization, a function of temperature. The curve of $2K/J_s$ against temperature is shown in Fig. 4–2. In a sintered aggregate of crystals with their preferential directions randomly oriented, the coercive force $_JH_C$ would be half this value, i.e. K/J_s.

The above result is based on the assumption that only the magneto-crystalline anisotropy energy is involved. However, for single crystals of approximately spherical shape there exists a critical diameter above which the effective coercive force is reduced. This was apparently first examined experimentally by Koenigsberger (1947) in connection with the permanent magnetism of rocks. Néel (1947) and Stoner and Wohlfarth (1948) show that above the critical diameter more than one domain is formed and that a reduction of coercive force results from the formation of Bloch walls which modify the energy changes that occur on the application of an external field. When the crystal size is reduced towards the critical value so that the simpler model should apply it is indeed found that the coercive force increases rapidly. Kittel (1949) gives a useful survey of domain theory which is of interest in this connection.

Fig. 4–3 shows the curve of coercive force $\mu_{0J}H_C$ as a function of temperature for a very fine-grained sintered specimen of $BaFe_{12}O_{19}$, and it will be seen that it does not follow the same shape as the curve of Fig. 4–2, as would be expected from the simple theory : Went *et al.* attribute this to variation of Bloch wall mobility with temperature.

The critical diameter for single domains in $BaFe_{12}O_{19}$ crystals is of the order of one micron and is thus much more easily approached than the critical diameters for iron and cobalt, which are respectively about five and fifty times smaller.

During the sintering process in the manufacture of the oxide materials care is taken to prevent the formation of large crystals

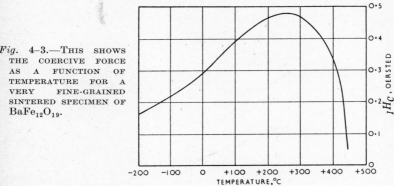

Fig. 4–3.—THIS SHOWS THE COERCIVE FORCE AS A FUNCTION OF TEMPERATURE FOR A VERY FINE-GRAINED SINTERED SPECIMEN OF $BaFe_{12}O_{19}$.

so that a large coercive force is obtained. Under these conditions the high value obtained for the coercive force as compared with conventional magnet steels can be attributed partly to the large anisotropy of the hexagonal crystal structure and also to the closer approach that can be made to the critical particle size.

The remanence of a magnet is of course highly dependent upon the saturation magnetization of the crystals. It can readily be shown by integration over a hemisphere, that for a homogenous isotropic magnetic material composed of domains with random orientation the remanent magnetization J_r of the material is approximately one half the saturation magnetization J_s of the crystals. The experimental results given by Went *et al.* confirm this in the case of $BaFe_{12}O_{19}$ as shown in Fig. 4–4.

Saturation Magnetization

We shall now discuss the factors governing J_s for oxides of the magnetoplumbite group, using $BaFe_{12}O_{19}$ as an example. Although we are considering the hexagonal ferrites we can draw to a large extent on the knowledge which has accumulated of the cubic ferrites which are magnetically " soft," for there is a close similarity between the two groups regarding the origin of the saturation magnetization.

The cubic ferrites crystallize in the structure, known as

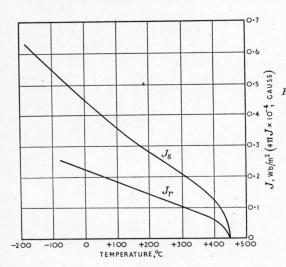

Fig. 4–4.—CURVES SHOW-
ING HOW THE REMA-
NENT MAGNETIZATION
OF MAGNETIC MATERIAL
($BaFe_{12}O_{19}$) IS APPROXI-
MATELY ONE HALF THE
SATURATION MAGNETI-
ZATION OF THE CRYS-
TALS.

" spinel," so called after the mineral $MgAl_2O_4$. In this arrangement, the oxygen ions form a closely packed cubic structure, the interstices between the oxygen ions providing two distinct kinds of site for the metal ions. These positions are known as tetrahedral and octahedral sites, being surrounded by four and six oxygen ions respectively. Néel (1948) showed that there is a strong tendency for anti-parallel alignment of the free electron spins of ions in adjacent dissimilar sites. Since the distances between adjacent sites are too large for the normal quantum mechanical exchange interactions to be appreciable, Néel attributed this phenomenon of " ferri-magnetism " to a super-exchange interaction, first proposed by Kramers (1934), in which the oxygen anions provide an essential link. Anderson (1950) has extended the theory quantitatively.

Without going too deeply into details, which may be found in the literature referred to in the bibliography, it may be said that the existence of metal ions with different saturation magnetic moments in the two kinds of site gives rise to a nett magnetic moment for the whole crystal which is less than would be expected from simple addition of the individual ionic moments, because of the anti-parallel alignment of adjacent dissimilar sites. This results in a material with a lower saturation magnetization than is customary for metal magnets.

Application of Ferrite Magnets

Although ferrite permanent magnets have a value of $(BH)_{max}$ considerably less than that of modern anisotropic metal magnets, there are many applications where the peculiar properties of the former give them distinct advantages over the more conventional materials, particularly where the largest magnetic energies are not required.

The chief advantage arises out of the large coercive force obtainable with ferrite magnets, and the consequent resistance to self-demagnetization. This makes it possible for the magnets to be magnetized free of their yokes or polepieces and fitted into the latter after the magnetization process, without any appreciable loss in flux. The reason for this may be deduced from Fig. 4–1. Any short magnet working into a large air gap will produce a strong reverse field tending to drive its working point down towards $_BH_C$. In the case of a normal metal magnet (b) (Fig. 4–1), the magnetization J is reduced considerably under these conditions since $_BH_C$ and $_JH_C$ are almost coincident. The reduction of J is an irreversible phenomenon and the subsequent closing of the air gap by a low reluctance yoke does little to restore J ; the operating point merely moves up a recoil curve on the B/H characteristic. In the case of the ferrite magnet with its large coercive force however, J is hardly reduced even when the operating point moves right back to $_BH_C$, which is the limit to which the magnet can attempt to demagnetize itself. Consequently, the introduction of a low-reluctance yoke allows the induction B to return almost to the value it would have if the magnet had been magnetized in the yoke. In order to demag-

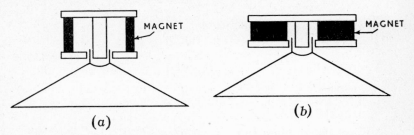

Fig. 4–5.—LOUDSPEAKER UNITS INCORPORATING TWO TYPES OF MAGNET, *i.e.*
METAL RING MAGNET, AND FERRITE MAGNET ASSEMBLY.

netize the specimen it is necessary to apply a very large reverse
field. It is, in fact, impracticable to demagnetize ferrite permanent magnets in the conventional manner with an alternating
field ; the usual way is to heat the specimen to a temperature
above the Curie point.

Operating Point

Neglecting the effect of leakage flux, $(BH)_{max}$ is obtained when
the operating point of the magnet is at about half the B-coercive
force. This follows from the fact that the BH curve is almost a
straight line for a ferrite magnet. Under these conditions the
magnet operates at a low induction B and a large demagnetizing
field as compared with a normal metal magnet. Thus for efficient
operation ferrite magnets are much shorter and of larger cross-
section than equivalent metal magnets. In fact they generally
take the form of discs rather than of rods, and this necessitates
an original approach to the design of units to incorporate them.

An example is given in Fig. 4–5, which shows loudspeaker units
incorporating the two types of magnet : (*a*) shows a typical
arrangement for a normal metal magnet ring, and (*b*) the form of
construction used for a ferrite magnet assembly.

Fig. 4–5 (*b*) also illustrates a property of ferrite magnets related
to leakage flux. It can be seen that the inside edge of the magnet
is very close to the centre polepiece. With a metal magnet it is
necessary to have a fairly large air gap between the side of the
magnet and any adjacent magnetic material to avoid excessive
leakage flux. Leakage flux due to adjacent polepieces is much
lower with a ferrite magnet, for its incremental permeability is
only fractionally greater than unity and the material thus has a

Fig. 4–6.—TYPICAL PERMANENT-MAGNET FOCUSING UNIT FOR TELEVISION
RECEIVERS, USING MULLARD MAGNADUR NON-METALLIC RING MAGNETS
(SHOWN ON RIGHT).

(Mullard Ltd.)

high reluctance which effectively reduces the leakage under these
conditions. Normal magnet steels have a permeability of the
order of four or more when working at their optimum point.

Ferrite permanent magnets have advantages over cast-metal
magnets in assemblies where considerable vibration is encountered,
e.g. in cycle dynamos, for they have greater resistance to demagnetization by mechanical shock. This is of particular importance
in applications where the magnet works into a fairly large air gap.

A most important advantage of the barium ferrites is the low
cost of the raw materials. A ferrite magnet may replace a metal
magnet in many applications with an appreciable saving in cost.
Typical examples of this are magnetic oil filters, and children's
toys incorporating magnets.

The high electrical resistivity of the ferrite magnets and their
consequent low eddy-current losses in alternating fields make
them very suitable for providing a polarizing field in inductors
and transformers. Examples are unidirectional pulse transformers, polarized relays, and microphone and telephone units.
A further advantage is the comparatively short length of magnet
required, leading to a reduction in the effective air gap introduced
into the transformer.

Because of their resistance to demagnetization by external fields, ferrite magnets can be used in opposing pairs to provide a field of strength variable with their relative position. This principle has been used in the focusing of television receivers, and could be applied also to the control of inductance in variable reactors.

References

ADELSKÖLD, V. *Arkiv für Kemi, Mineralogi och Geologi* (Upsala) 12A, 1938, **29**, 1–9.

AMINOFF, G. *Geologiska Föreningens Förhandlingar*, 1925, **47**, III, 283–9.

ANDERSON, P. W. *Physical Review*, 1950, **79**, 705.

BOZORTH, R. M. " Ferromagnetism," 1951.

BROCKMAN, F. G. *Electrical Engineering*, 1952, **7**, 64.

CHITTY, M. W. G. British Patent Spec. No. 594474, 1945.

KATO, Y., and TAKEI, T. *J. Inst. Elec. Engrs.* (Japan), 1933, **53**, 408.

KITTEL, C. *Rev. Modern Physics*, 1949, **21**, 541.

KOENIGSBERGER, J. G. *Phil. Mag.*, 1947, **38**, 640.

KRAMERS, H. A. *Physica*, 1934, **1**, 182.

NÉEL, L. *Ann. Physique*, 1948, **3**, 137 ; *C.R. Acad. Sci. Paris*, 1947, **224**, 1488, 1550 ; 1947, **225**, 109.

NEPPIRAS, E. A. *J. Sci. Inst.*, 1953, **30**, 72.

SOCIETE D'ELECTRO CHIMIE D'UGINE. British Patent Spec. No. 596875, 1943/45.

STONER, E. C., and WOHLFARTH, E. P. *Phil. Trans. Roy. Soc.*, 1948, **240A**, 599.

TAKEI, T., YASUDA, T., and ISHIHARA, S. *Electrotech. J.* (Japan), 1940, **4**,.75.

WENT, J. J., RATHENAU, G. W., GORTER, E. W., and VAN OOSTERHOUT, G. W. *Philips Tech. Rev.*, 1952, **13**, 194.

5. MAGNETIC POWDER CORES

By

C. Gordon Smith, M.A., A.M.I.E.E.

The use of magnetic materials in the form of "dust" or compressed powder cores * has been established for some 30 years and has been until recently confined to purposes to meet the specialized requirements of telecommunication. Such uses, to be described below, generally involve the magnetically soft materials† developed for use at low inductions, although, as will be shown, the effective properties of these materials become modified as a result of the form and condition in which they are used.

Historical Development

Reference in 1887 to the use of iron filings embedded in wax was made by Heaviside,[1] who found that the inductance of a coil could be increased by such means without causing any appreciable dissipation of energy. The magnetic properties of iron powder in various forms were investigated in the early twentieth century, but little successful application developed until the First World War. It was then that the need arose for alternative and improved substitutes for the cores of telephone loading coils, which hitherto had been made from bundles of steel wire. The development of a new production technique for compressed magnetic powder cores was successfully completed by the Western Electric Company [2] of America, the main features of the process being the production of a suitable (electrolytic) iron powder and the use of high compacting pressures in conjunction with special insulating binders. Improved cores of this type are now used as essential components in telephone and radio equipment. Important stages of progress in the art were the discovery of the specially suitable properties of carbonyl-iron powder in Germany [3] and later, in the U.S.A., the application of the nickel-iron alloys.[4] Further improvements followed to satisfy the technical requirements of

---

* The use of the term "dust" core, although generally accepted, is somewhat to be deprecated, particularly owing to the recent application of ultra-fine magnetic particles in the production of permanent magnets. (See Section 3 (b).)

† The recent applications of ferrites in these fields is described in Section 2 (b).

the widening applications in the development of carrier telephony at increasingly higher frequencies. The successful application of powder cores to broadcast radio receivers by Vogt [5] in 1932 was achieved through important new concepts in core design and manufacture.

Elementary Theory of Magnetic Powder Cores

The principal aim is usually the production of an inductor of low power-factor ; the introduction of a ferromagnetic core assists by reducing the resistance of the requisite winding in proportion to its magnetic permeability, but this advantage will be partially offset by losses occurring in the magnetic material. The two factors must thus be carefully balanced to achieve optimum results.

(a) *Permeability.* It will be assumed that the working conditions involve alternating magnetic fields of low density in the region in which the incremental permeability is substantially constant. Such conditions usually apply in most practical applications, the flux density being in the region of 1 mWb/m² (10 gauss) or less.

It is first necessary to consider the relationship between the effective permeability μ_c of the core material, and the intrinsic permeability μ_i of the ferromagnetic component. A further quantity referred to loosely as effective permeability, μ_e, relates only to a particular coil assembly, and is defined by the ratio L/L_o, where L is the inductance of the coil plus core and L_o is the inductance of the same coil but with core removed.

In the more familiar case of a core built up of high permeability laminations, $\mu_c \simeq \mu_i \simeq \mu_e$, as the differences are due to flux leakage, which is relatively small. In the powder core, however, $\mu_c \ll \mu_i$ on account of gaps in the magnetic path. Furthermore, owing to the relatively low values of μ_c, leakage flux may be appreciable, with the result that μ_e may be considerably less than μ_c.*

The calculation of the relationship between μ_i and μ_c has been the subject of much study [8] based on various assumptions, e.g. that the particles are uniform spheres, cubes, laminæ, etc., but none of these approach closely the effects obtained in practice on account of the wide variation of particle size and shape obtain-

* For example in the type of core illustrated in Fig. 5–2 (B), μ_i might be 500 with μ_c 20 and μ_e about 4·0.

ing in all metal powders. A simple analysis without considering such details will, however, be informative. Suppose the magnetic circuit to be of unit length and divided longitudinally into a portion g of unit permeability (i.e. air-gap), and a portion $(1 - g)$ of permeability μ_i, then

$$\mu_c = \frac{\mu_i}{g(\mu_i - 1) + 1}.$$

Curves of this function are shown in Fig. 5–1, covering a practical range of variation in μ_c and g.

Except for low values of the intrinsic permeability μ_i, which are not likely to be of practical interest, the effective permeability is mainly influenced by the value of g rather than by μ_i. This explains an important subsidiary property of dust cores, namely, constancy of permeability. The usual causes of permeability variation, e.g. flux density, temperature, magnetic shock, etc., are reduced to small proportions owing to the diluting effect of the magnetic gap. The same fact indicates what considerations should be made when selecting the most appropriate magnetic powders and methods of core manufacture, where effective permeability is the prime consideration. The problem is usually the reduction of the gap effect ; this is achieved by using high compacting pressures, a minimum of insulating binder, and a magnetic powder which is easily compressible, i.e. whose particles are soft enough to deform, and so prevent formation of voids in the core, and whose degree of subdivision is no greater than necessary to restrict eddy-current losses adequately. A high intrinsic permeability of the metal is usually of secondary importance.

(b) *Loss Factors.* In the majority of applications the power factor of the inductor is of major importance and consideration must be given to the losses introduced by the ferromagnetic powder. To a fair approximation, at the low flux densities for which the incremental permeability is constant, for frequencies below a few megacycles per second, and excluding materials with unusually large or small losses, the effective series loss-resistance R_e in ohms due to the core may be expressed as *

$$R_e = 2\pi f L \mu_c \left(\frac{aB}{10^4} + c + ef \right)$$

* A similar analysis is given by Kersten.[10] Both analyses assume a magnetic circuit without leakage (e.g. a toroidal core).

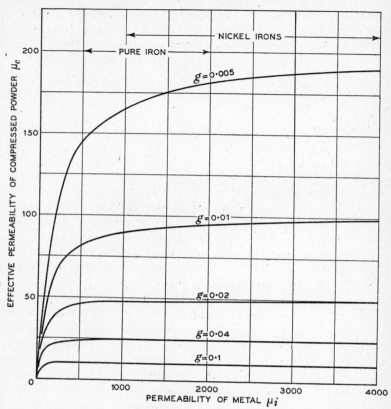

Fig. 5–1.—Relationship between intrinsic and effective permeabilities for different gap effects.

where f = frequency, c/s.
          L = effective inductance, H.
          a = hysteresis loss constant* ⎫
          c = residual loss constant   ⎬ relating to the
          e = eddy-current loss constant ⎭   core material.
          B = r.m.s. flux density, Wb/m².

The Q-factor, or " goodness factor," Q of a coil is given by

$$Q = 2\pi f L/(R_e + R_o),$$

where R_o is the winding resistance, which for a given inductance is inversely proportional to μ_c.

* The exponent x in the Steinmetz formula, loss $= \eta B^x$ has a value of 2·0.

The manner in which both hysteresis and residual losses affect the Q-factor is independent of frequency, and the residual loss and eddy-current contributions are independent of the size of the core. The hysteresis effect is, however, related to the core size in that the flux density B is dependent on the core dimensions for a given magnetizing current in the inductance. The eddy-current loss increases with frequency and tends to preponderate as the frequency is raised. The d.c. winding resistance will also be inversely proportional to the size of the core. Other factors entering into the design of high-Q coils are the further I^2R losses in the winding due to skin and proximity effects, and dielectric losses; both may become appreciable even at relatively low frequencies (e.g. 10 kc/s). For fuller analyses of loss distribution and general principles of design the reader is referred to publications by Legg and Given [9] and Kersten, [10] and to the textbook by Welsby. [11]

Applications and Uses of Magnetic Powder Cores

The original commercial application of magnetic powder cores was for telephone loading coils, i.e. inductors inserted at regular intervals in telephone cables to decrease signal attenuation. The technical requirements for these, which must be met in a limited space for economic reasons, are constant inductance and high Q-factor. The introduction of high-frequency carrier telephony has resulted in a tendency to abandon line loading, but there exists a further demand for similar high-grade inductors in terminal filtering equipment. A secondary consideration is the requirement for low hysteresis loss, which, apart from its energy dissipation, may produce non-linear distortion and cross-modulation between carrier circuits. [12]

For all these applications it is usual to use toroidal cores, although such a design is not efficient from the point of view of d.c. resistance. With any other form of core, even if completely shrouded, considerable magnetic leakage will take place on account of the relatively low permeability of the compressed powder ; this leads to considerable inefficiency in the magnetic circuit and to stray fields which may cause coupling with neighbouring components. Again, although reasonably strong mechanically, powder-core materials do not lend themselves to fabrication or machining ; the toroid is a form easily made by a pressing without joints in the magnetic circuit. With available

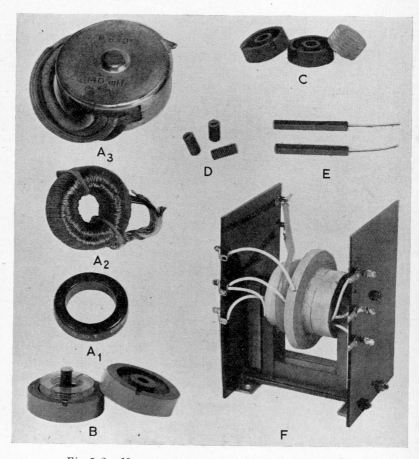

Fig. 5–2.—MAGNETIC POWDER CORES OF VARIOUS TYPES.

A_1 Toroidal core of high-permeability alloy powder for small loading-coil.

A_2 Wound coil on A_1.

A_3 Completed coil in screening can ; Q-factor of about 100 at 1,500 c/s.

B   Large " pot " core showing winding former for carrier-frequency applications : $Q > 300$ from 50 kc/s to 2 Mc/s.

C   Small " pot " core for carrier and radio applications : $Q > 200$ from 80 kc/s to 3 Mc/s.

D   Small screw cores for radio applications : effective permeability about 2 ; $Q > 150$ from 500 kc/s to 20 Mc/s ; > 100 up to 50 Mc/s.

E   Permeability-tuning radio cores ; effective permeability about 10.

F   Television line-frequency transformer, wound on core of high-permeability iron-powder pressings.

(*By courtesy of Salford Electrical Instruments Ltd.*)

materials it is easily possible to design toroidal inductors with Q-factors of 200–300 (i.e. power factors of less than $\frac{1}{2}$ per cent.) at all frequencies above a few hundred c/s up to several hundred kc/s.

Powder cores in radio receivers can supply the need for high-Q inductors for tuning circuits, but their use is based more on economic considerations in providing a given selectivity at less expense or in a smaller space.

For broadcast frequencies and above, small cylindrical cores of a variety of shapes and sizes are used, giving similar Q-factors, reduction in size being possible because of the preponderance of eddy-current losses at high frequencies, for which the effective resistance is independent of core dimensions.

For the lower radio (i.e. broadcast receiver intermediate) frequencies or for high-frequency carrier telephony, a compromise is often made in the form of cores completely or partially shrouding a winding (see Fig. 5–2 (C)).

Besides these main functions of powder cores, subsidiary but important uses have developed mainly in the r.f. fields. These depend on the possibilities of inductance variation by the relative motion of core and coil. There are inherent limitations on the range of possible adjustment ; because the toroidal form is impossible, only a fraction of the effective permeability of the core materials can be utilized. Where the maximum range is desired it is necessary to use a cylindrical core with a large length/diameter ratio, which restricts the Q-factor. However, cores giving an inductance ratio of 10/1 have been successfully made for radio receiver tuning (see Fig. 5–2 (E)).

In other instances it is useful to have a means for the precise adjustment of a fixed inductor. This is often required, particularly at the higher radio frequencies where any capacitance additional to the self-capacitance of the circuit components is undesirable. It can effectively be provided by a movable core with moulded thread to engage in a suitable coil former.

Another application in which powder cores may offer important advantages is in devices such as receiving loops for direction-finding equipment, where the introduction of a magnetic core into the loop will give increased sensitivity.[6]

High-Permeability Powder Cores

Attention has recently been given to the development of

powder cores of specially high permeability, at the expense of increased losses. Such materials may be made from inexpensive but readily compressible and relatively coarse iron powder, sometimes in the form of flake.[13] They have uses at power frequencies as inexpensive replacements for silicon-iron (Stalloy) stampings in small transformers, reactors, etc., in which power loss is unimportant. They also bridge the gap between dust cores and normal laminations. In general their hysteresis losses are high compared with those of silicon-iron and similar laminations, but eddy-current losses are reduced. An important application in television receivers is to line-frequency transformers for providing the e.h.t. voltage.[14] A high permeability is required to obtain adequate coupling, and under these circumstances lower losses can be obtained than with silicon-iron stampings. Another use is for the moulded pole pieces for electromagnetic deflectors for television cathode-ray tubes.

A typical selection of coils and cores is shown in Fig. 5–2.

Magnetic Powder Core Materials

From the foregoing it will be evident that the properties required of a magnetic powder are that the particles shall be easily compressible to form a dense core, and that the particle size be fine enough to reduce eddy-current losses effectively, but not too fine, for otherwise difficulty will be found in producing an adequate core permeability. The intrinsic permeability is not of first importance ; the metal should, however, have low hysteresis loss and a high resistivity in order further to limit eddy losses. Constancy of properties with temperature and resistance to magnetic shock may be of importance, as, although these factors themselves are very largely looked after by the magnetic dilution effect, a very high order of excellence may be needed in precision applications such as loading coils and inductors for filters for carrier telephony.

In practice the main materials used are special iron powders and nickel-iron and related ternary-alloy powders.

Iron Powders

(a) *Carbonyl Iron Powder*. Carbonyl iron powders were among the first to be used extensively for high-quality dust cores. Their special characteristics [15] include a spherical shape and uniformity of particle size, combined with a peculiar metallurgical structure yielding eddy-current losses considerably lower than those of an iron-carbon alloy of similar composition. The characteristics are ideally suitable for use at radio frequencies. Hysteresis loss is also low, but although the spherical shape gives a good packing factor, the high mechanical hardness (an estimated diamond pyramid number of over 800) makes compression difficult and thus it is difficult to obtain high core permeability. This disadvantage can be overcome by heat treatment of the powder to remove carbon, but even then the small particle size limits the permeability obtainable. Eddy current and hysteresis losses are somewhat increased by the heat treatment. Nevertheless, the decarburized grades of carbonyl-iron powders are still used for a number of low-frequency applications, although in this country and the U.S.A. the use of nickel-iron powders [16] has become more general.

(b) *Electrolytic Iron Powder.* This type of powder is made by the mechanical disintegration of a brittle electro-deposit. It has a relatively high degree of purity although particle size and shape are unfavourable from the point of view of powder-core considerations. Its use for powder cores has now become restricted to purposes for which relatively high losses can be tolerated.

(c) *Hydrogen-reduced Iron Powder.* The reduction of iron oxide by hydrogen at suitable temperatures provides an alternative means of producing a pure iron powder. Although very fine particles may be obtained, their magnetic properties are generally inferior to those of carbonyl-iron powder, eddy-current losses being higher both inherently and on account of difficulties of insulating the characteristically irregular and porous particles. These powders are applied for second-grade high-frequency cores, particularly when effective permeability is more important than high Q-values, the softness of the powder favouring a high compressibility at the expense of eddy-current losses.

(d) *Flake-iron Powders.* A recent development,[13] intended to bridge the gap between powder cores and laminated materials, has resulted from the use of iron in the form of thin flakes aligned so that their major planes fall parallel to the lines of flux, giving permeability dilution controlled by the larger dimensions of the flakes, but eddy-current losses controlled by the thickness. Such materials have in general rather higher losses than powder cores or thin alloy laminations, but they are finding a number of applications in new fields as indicated above.

(e) *Miscellaneous.* Other methods have been used for the production of iron powders but are of little current interest. The Hametag process involves the mechanical disintegration of chopped wire and produces a rather coarse flattened particle ; such material had some application in Germany for the production of iron powder cores with permeability rather higher than can be obtained from carbonyl powders.

Other methods include the disintegration of the molten metal. Such processes are used for the production of an inexpensive powder for metallurgical purposes, but the products are of little use for cores.

Nickel-Iron and Related Alloy Powders

Although the main feature of these alloys, their exceptionally high initial permeability, is not of first importance, their excellent subsidiary magnetic properties of low hysteresis and residual losses have led to successful applications in compressed powder form, in the frequency range of line-telecommunication equipment.

These alloys are tough and ductile and their preparation in powder form have presented some special problems. Two main methods have been satisfactorily evolved. The first [4] relies on the artificial embrittlement by intergranular penetration of a small addition of sulphur followed by mechanical disintegration and thermal treatment. The second [17] method involves the hydrogen reduction of the mixed oxides followed by a combination of thermal and mechanical treatments to ensure thorough metallurgical homogeneity. Further problems involve the use of refractory insulating binders so that cores may be given a suitable annealing treatment after pressing, to restore the optimum magnetic properties. Molybdenum-Permalloy and nickel-copper-iron alloy powders have both been satisfactorily applied and have made possible the production of high-permeability cores of outstanding quality for loading coils of small size and high efficiency. These form an essential component in telephone distribution networks not only in trunk systems but also in heavily developed urban areas.

A further advantage of the nickel-iron alloys (notably in the

TABLE 1. MAGNETIC POWDER CORE MATERIALS

Material	Relative permeability	Loss Factors			Applications
	μ	$a \times 10^6$	$c \times 10^6$	$e \times 10^{10}$	
Compressed at high pressures, e.g. 100 tons/in.²					
Electrolytic iron . .	35	50	100	850	Early loading coils (obsolete).
Carbonyl-iron, E type . .	15	3	200	2	Low-loss coils for filter and loading application at high frequencies where minimum hysteresis required.
Carbonyl-iron, C type . .	50	10	200	20	Loading coils general use (mainly Continental).
Permalloy, C powder .	125	1·6	30	200	Loading coils with special high permeability for use in restricted space.
(Nickel-iron-molybdenum)	60	2·5	50	100	Loading coils, general use.
	25	7·0	100	80	Low-loss coils for filter and loading application at high frequencies where minimum hysteresis required.
With different proportions of binder.	14	10	150	70	
Sendust (aluminium-silicon-iron).	60	5	200	30	Loading coils for general use (restricted).
Flake-iron and electrolytic. (Special insulation technique.)	150–250	300	—	30–100	(Rough estimation.) Applications at power frequencies and where losses unimportant.
Compressed at lower pressure, e.g. 20 tons/in.²					
Electrolytic iron, <325 mesh.	16	250	1,200	200	(Little used.)
Carbonyl-iron, E type . .	12	3	200	2	Radio frequencies : first-grade cores.
Carbonyl-iron, F type (special fine particle size).	10	2	100	<2	Radio frequencies (above 10 Mc/s).
Hydrogen-reduced iron . .	20	50	750	30	Radio frequencies, where permeability more important than losses, permeability tuning, etc.

range 35 to 50 per cent. nickel) for dust cores is their high resistivity, which favours low eddy-current losses. These alloys have found some application in the high-frequency field, but the difficulty of producing sufficiently fine powders has hindered competition with carbonyl-iron powders at radio frequencies.

Iron-Aluminium-Silicon Alloys

Certain iron-aluminium-silicon [18] alloys, investigated originally in Japan, were found to have the characteristics of " soft " magnetic materials although mechanically hard and brittle, facilitating reduction to powder. These alloys were further developed in Germany [7] during the Second World War and had some measure of success, principally on the grounds of nickel economy. The magnetic properties do not, however, compete with the best nickel-iron and related alloys.

Table 1 gives details of the magnetic properties of the principle core materials together with notes on their applications.

M.A.F.

M

References

1. HEAVISIDE, O. " Notes on the Theory of the Telephone and on Hysteresis," *Electrician*, 1887, **18**, 302–3.
2. SPEED, B., and ELMEN, G. W. " Magnetic Properties of Compressed Powder Iron," *Trans. A.I.E.E.*, 1921, **40**, 596.
3. British Patent 269770 (1926).
4. SHACKLETON, W. J., and BARBER, I. G. " Compressed Powdered Permalloy : Manufacture and Magnetic Properties," *Trans. A.I.E.E.*, 1928, **47**, 429.
   LEGG, V. E., and GIVEN, H. J. " Compressed Powdered Molybdenum-Permalloy for High Quality Inductance Coils," *Bell System Tech. Jnl.*, 1940, **19**, 385–406.
5. VOGT, H. " New Development in Tuning Coils ; Inductances of Remarkably High Efficiency using ' Ferrocart ' Cores," *Wireless World*, 1932, **31**, 272–273.
6. UMPELBY, R. F., *et al.* " Iron Cores, D.F. Loops and Manufacture of Iron Dust," *B.I.O.S.* Final Report No. 1203. H.M.S.O.
7. HENSEL, F. R. " Iron Cores," *F.I.A.T.* Final Report No. 792. H.M.S.O.
8. HOWE, G. W. O., *et al.* " Permeability of Iron Dust Cores," *Wireless Engineer*, Nov. 1946, **23**, and Feb. 1947, **24**.
9. LEGG, V. E. " Magnetic Measurements at Low Flux Densities," *Bell System Tech. Jnl.*, 1936, **15**, 39–62.
10. KERSTEN, M. " Spulen mit Massekernen " (Coils with Dust Cores), *Elektrotechnische Zeitschrift*, 1937, **58**, 1335–38, 1364–67.
11. WELSBY, V. G. " Theory of Design of Inductance Coils," Macdonald & Co., London, 1950.
12. PETERSON, E. " Harmonic Production in Ferromagnetic Materials at Low Frequencies and Low Flux Densities," *Bell System Tech. Jnl.*, 1928, **7**, 762.
13. CAMPBELL, G., and WOOD, F. J. " A Laminated Flake Iron Material for use at Audio and Ultrasonic Frequencies," " Soft Magnetic Materials in Telecommunications," ed., Richards, C. E., and Lynch, A. C., pp. 268–277. Pergamon Press, London, 1943.
14. FRIEND, A. W. " Molded Iron Dust Cores for use in Horizontal Deflection Circuits," *R.C.A. Review*, March 1947, **8**, 98–115.
15. PFEIL, L. B., POLGREEN, G. R., and BUCKLEY, S. E. *Symposium on Powder Metallurgy, Iron & Steel Institute Special Report No. 38*, 1947, Section C, 47–59.
16. RICHARDS, C. E. A., BUCKLEY, S. E., BARDELL, P. R., and LYNCH, A. C. " Some Properties and Tests of Magnetic Powders and Powder Cores." Symposium of Papers on Ferromagnetic Materials, Session IV, *Proc. I.E.E.*, **97**, Part II, No. 56, April 1950, 236–45.
17. POLGREEN, G. E. " The Production and Application of Magnetic Powders," *G.E.C. Journal*, '19, July 1952, No. 3, pp. 152–69.
18. MASUMOTO, H. " Magnetic and Electrical Properties of a New Alloy, ' Sendust,' " *Sci. Repts.*, Tohoku Imp. Univ., 1936, 388–402.

6. NON-MAGNETIC FERROUS AND MAGNETIC-COMPENSATING ALLOYS

By

C. Gordon Smith, M.A., A.M.I.E.E.

NON-MAGNETIC FERROUS ALLOYS

In the construction of electrical equipment where materials with non-magnetic properties are desirable or essential, and where the mechanical properties of non-ferrous alloys are inadequate, use is made of special non-magnetic steels or cast irons.

Non-Magnetic Steels

Although the effect of the addition of non-magnetic alloying elements to iron is to reduce the magnetic permeability, in general appreciable magnetic properties will be retained after the proportion of alloying element has been increased to such an extent that the characteristic mechanical properties are lost. However, the desired results may be obtained by making use of the special effect of the lowering of the Curie point, particularly remarkable in certain nickel-iron and related alloys. The singular characteristics of these alloys was first observed in 1889 by Hopkinson,[19] who found a 25 per cent. nickel-iron alloy to be non-magnetic. Fig. 6–1, after Merica,[20] gives a simplified version of the diagram of the nickel-iron system, and shows the rapid lowering of the Curie point in the region of 30 per cent. nickel. It should be noted, however, that complications exist in the region below about 35 per cent. nickel in that the alloys may exist in two states with irreversible or very slow transformation rates. This peculiarity was also observed by Hopkinson, who found that his 25 per cent. nickel-steel became strongly magnetic on cooling below room temperature and remained so until re-heated to a high temperature. The addition of further elements such as carbon, chromium, manganese, etc., may however be used to assist in the stabilizing of the alloy in the non-magnetic (austenitic) form. Manganese is a particularly useful addition as its presence tends to lower the Curie point still further. Hopkinson's 25 per cent. nickel-iron can be made reasonably stable by the addition of 0·3 per cent. of carbon, and such an alloy has been considerably used.

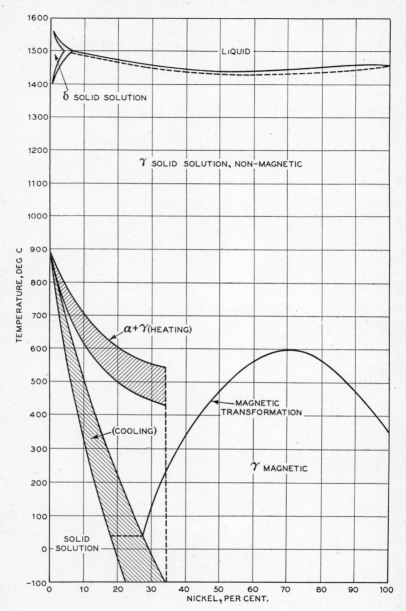

Fig. 6-1.—Simplified diagram of the nickel-iron system (Merica).

More recently increasing use has been made of a number of highly alloyed nickel-steels, including chromium or manganese, or both together, which give improved tensile properties in addition to the non-magnetic characteristic. Included in this group are the well-known austenitic stainless steels, but unless the proportion of alloying elements is adequate, the effect of cold work, useful in improving the tensile properties, may reintroduce magnetic properties [21] by the formation of a certain proportion of ferrite particles distributed throughout the austenitic matrix. (Compare the use of this phenomenon in wires for magnetic recording : see p. 181.)

The principal uses of non-magnetic steels are for parts of electrical machinery, such as retaining rings for alternator rotor caps and wedges, armature binding wire and strip, and armouring for a.c. cables. In the majority of such applications alternating magnetic fields are involved, and further advantage is often found in the resistivity which limits eddy-current losses.

Non-Magnetic Cast Irons

In a similar manner, non-magnetic properties may be conferred on cast iron by the inclusion of a proportion of alloying elements ; the two main commercially established alloys are Nomag and Ni-Resist (see Table 1). These find application in the electrical industry where a less expensive material than a non-magnetic steel is needed and where conditions of use and production call for a casting. They have the additional advantage of higher resistivities than the steels and are frequently used for heavy starter resistance grids, covers for switchgear and other parts in which the effect of induced currents is to be limited. The recent development of the production of cast iron containing graphite in spheroidal form,[22] which gives most pronounced improvement in mechanical properties, has been satisfactorily applied to the production of non-magnetic materials. (In this case, however, some reduction in electrical resistivity results from the compact graphite structure.)

In all the above alloys the non-magnetic properties are due to the particular metallurgical structure occurring above the Curie point, so that on cooling to low temperatures the magnetic properties will reappear. There appears to be little information available concerning precise values of the Curie temperatures ;

TABLE 1. NON-MAGNETIC FERROUS ALLOYS *

Material	Composition (Approx. main alloying additions)	Magnetic permeability	Resistivity ohm-m	Approx. ultimate tensile strength tons/in.^{2}	Notes
Cast irons					
Nomag (Ferranti Ltd.)	6% Mn, 10% Ni	1·03	1·50	12–16	British Patent 204,598. (Expired.)
Ni-Resist. (Various manufacturers.)	14% Ni, 7% Cu, 1·5% Mn, 2% Cr.	1·03	1·40	10–14	British Patent 281,051. (Expired.)
Steels					
Non-magnetic steel. (Clyde Alloy Steel Co.)	(a) 8% Ni, 8% Mn, 8% Cr. / (b) 4% Ni, 8% Mn, 8% Cr.	1·003	0·76	60	(a) High-strength steels for rotor end caps, etc. / (b) Modified composition with similar properties.
N.M.C. Steel. (Firth Vickers.)	10% Ni, 5% Mn, 4% Cr.	1·008/1·03		65	Original function as high-expansion steel. Ministry of Supply D.T.D. Spec. 247.
Stainless steels					
Staybrite. (Thos. Firth & J. Brown Ltd.)	8% Ni, 18% Cr.	1·005/1·03	0·72	45	B.S. 58A, etc.
Silver Fox (20). (Samuel Fox & Co.)		1·08/1·13			In cold-worked condition 10% reduction.
Anka (Brown-Bayley Ltd.). and other similar alloys .	12% Ni, 18% Cr.	1·4 / about 10 / 1·003 / 1·11 / 1·7	0·80	60 / 100 / 40	In cold-worked condition 20% reduction. / In cold-worked condition 50% reduction. / In the soft condition. / In cold-worked condition 50% reduction. / In cold-worked condition 90% reduction.
	12% Ni, 25% Cr.	1·003 / 1·005	0·90		In the soft condition. / In cold-worked condition 90% reduction.

* These materials have the general characteristics of paramagnetic materials, permeability being independent of flux density. Permeability is expressed relative to that of free space.

some evidence has been found with regard to phase changes taking place at the temperature of boiling oxygen ($-$ 180° C.) in some of the alloys referred to below ; in one of the less stable alloys examined, non-magnetic properties were still found at the temperature of solid carbon dioxide ($-$ 80° C.).

Table 1 gives details of materials at present commercially available.

MAGNETIC COMPENSATING ALLOYS

Magnetic compensating alloys, like the non-magnetic irons and steels, depend for their special properties on the effects of their relatively low magnetic transformation temperatures. For these alloys, however, materials are selected with Curie points slightly above working temperature, so that a rapid change of magnetic properties (e.g. permeability and saturation values) with temperature results.

Applications

Such alloys find application in the construction of electricity meters and speedometers whose indications are required to be independent of temperature. In the electricity meter,[23] considerable temperature-errors would be introduced by the relatively high resistance/temperature coefficient of the eddy-current braking disc ; with the usual aluminium disc an increase in speed of 0·4 per cent. per °C. would result from the reduced braking effect. A further, smaller, error in the same direction is likely to be caused by the reduction in flux in the permanent-magnet system. The method of compensation adopted is to arrange, across the poles of the permanent magnet, a diverter magnetic shunt having a reluctance which increases appropriately with temperature. The desired characteristics can be obtained from a variety of alloys with Curie points not much above normal ambient temperatures. The useful characteristics of the nickel-iron series can again be employed ; other alloys also used are those from the nickel-copper series in the region of 70 per cent. nickel.*

These alloys may be used in a similar manner to compensate

* The materials should be specially made to meet appropriate magnetic specifications, as without special precautions the magnetic properties of alloys made commercially for other applications may show wide variations.

speedometers of the " drag disc " type.[24] In such cases the main deflectional force is that caused by the eddy currents induced in an aluminium disc or cup by the rotation of a small permanent magnet. Without suitable magnetic compensation, temperature errors up to 10 per cent. might be found in automobile speedometers, and considerably more in aircraft equipment.

The same method of compensation can sometimes usefully be employed in conventional moving-coil electrical indicating instruments. Normally voltmeters are compensated by a series swamp-resistance of manganese or other alloy of low temperature coefficient, and ammeters usually include a copper shunt making temperature compensation unnecessary. Where high sensitivity is called for, as in pyrometer instruments for temperature indication from thermocouple output, magnetic compensation has advantages : a combined compensation for cold-junction temperature and instrument resistance variation can be arranged [25] with the use of temperature-sensitive magnetic alloys.

Low Curie-point alloys have been applied to temperature-operated relays. These may operate by the movement of an armature of which the position is determined by the counter forces of a spring (constant) and a magnet (temperature-dependent). Although bimetallic strip and other differential expansion devices are more usual, sometimes greater simplicity and convenience of design may be gained by the use of the magnetic method. Further applications are to the construction of small transformers and choke coils with temperature-independent output, or with special temperature characteristics, for compensation purposes in instrumentation.

Practical Alloys

The alloys used for these applications are usually those developed from the nickel-iron and nickel-copper systems. For compensation purposes a Curie point in the region of 80° C. to 100° C. will usually give the requisite variation over the normal range of ambient temperatures. From Fig. 6–1 it will be seen that the composition required for the appropriate Curie point approaches the region in which instability may occur. This difficulty has been overcome by the addition of chromium and/or other elements,[26] or by special processing.

A difficult problem in the production of such alloys is the

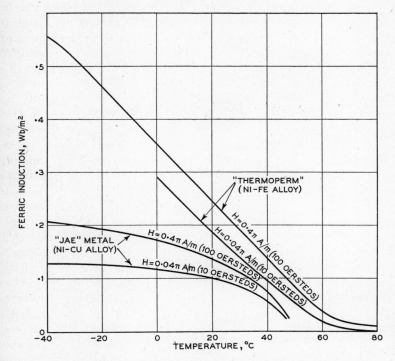

Fig. 6–2.—CHARACTERISTICS OF MAGNETIC COMPENSATING ALLOYS.

TABLE- 2. MAGNETIC COMPENSATING ALLOYS

Trade name	Manufacturer	Notes
Mutemp . .	Richard Thomas & Baldwins Ltd.	Nickel-iron alloy.
Telcon R2799 alloy	Telegraph Construction & Maintenance Co. Ltd.	Nickel-iron alloy.
Temperature Compensator 30.	Carpenter Steel Co., U.S.A.	Nickel-iron alloy, available in three grades.
Hoskins alloy 567 .	Hoskins Mfg. Co., U.S.A.	Nickel-iron alloy.
JAE metal . .	Henry Wiggin & Co. Ltd.	Nickel-copper alloy.
Calmaloy . .	G.E.C. of America .	Nickel-copper alloy. Originally called Thermalloy.
N.M.H.G. alloy .	Acieries d'Imphy, France	Nickel-iron alloy ; choice of compositions available for different temperature ranges.
Thermoperm .	Krupps, Germany .	Nickel-iron alloy.

extension of the operating range to cover the requirements of aircraft, etc., in which operating temperatures may vary over 100° C. or more. Another use with stringent demands is for domestic electricity meters for outside installation, a practice not uncommon outside Britain. A solution can sometimes be found by the combination of two or more alloys.

Nickel-copper alloys have also been used extensively for magnetic compensation. It has been stated that their properties are easier to control during manufacture ; their permeabilities are in general lower, but this can usually be circumvented by suitable shunt design. The temperature range over which a linear temperature/permeability relationship is obtainable is considerably lower ; for this reason future development would appear to be with the nickel-iron alloys.

Characteristics of typical alloys are shown in Fig. 6–2, and Table 2 gives a list of materials commercially available.

As regards special alloys for thermally operated relays, etc., with various Curie points, there appear to be few standardized materials commercially available, although there has been practical application of such alloys.[27]

References

19. HOPKINSON, J. " Magnetic Properties of Alloys of Nickel and Iron," *Proc. Royal Soc.* (Lond.), 1889–90, **47**, 23–4.
20. MERICA, P. D. " Constitution of Iron-Nickel Alloys," Amer. Soc. Metals Handbook, 1936, pp. 271–3.
21. AUSTIN, J. B., and MILLER, S. D. " Magnetic Permeability of some Austenitic Iron-Chromium-Nickel Alloys as Influenced by Heat Treatment and Cold Work," *Trans. Amer. Soc. for Metals*, Sept. 1940.
22. EVEREST, A. B. " Engineering Applications of Spheroidal Graphite Cast Iron," Paper to 4th International Mechanical Engineers' Congress, *Engineer*, 1952, **193**, June 13th and 20th, 794–5, 838–40.
23. KINNARD, I. F., and FAUS, H. T. " Temperature Errors in Induction Watt Hour Meters," *Trans. Amer. Inst. Elect. Engrs.*, 44, 1925, 275.
24. HINDLEY, W. N. " ' Thermoperm ' and Magnetic Tachometers," *B.I.O.S.* Final Report 1259, H.M.S.O.
25. KINNARD, I. F., and FAUS, H. T. " A Self-compensated Temperature Indicator," *Jnl. Amer. Inst. Elec. Engrs.*, 1930, **49**, 343–45.
26. JACKSON, L. I. R., and RUSSELL, H. W. " Temperature Sensitive Magnetic Alloys and Their Uses," *Instruments*, 1938, **2**, 279–82.
27. " Magnetic Fire Detector," *Engineering*, **169**, Feb. 10th, 1950, p. 161.

7. MAGNETIC RECORDING MATERIALS

By

C. Gordon Smith, M.A., A.M.I.E.E.

The original idea of the magnetic recording of sound is attributed to Poulsen. His invention, the "telegraphone," was covered by a Danish patent in 1899.[28] The essential features of this machine consisted of a helical coil of steel wire mounted on a rotating cylinder against which rested two small electromagnets respectively for recording and reproduction purposes.

Development of Magnetic Recording

Magnetic recording apparatus has altered little in principle since that time, but many advances have been achieved by careful design and the use of improved materials. Attention has been given to the theory of magnetic recording, and although the quantitative application of magnetic data in design has not proved very tractable, simple considerations give an indication of the properties required of the magnetic recording medium.

Essentially both the recording and reproducing mechanisms consist of a high-permeability magnetic core with a magnetizing winding and small air-gap, together with the recording medium in the form of a wire or tape which can be drawn past and in close proximity to the air-gap. The magnetic core is usually toroidal, as indicated in Fig. 7–1, and composed of nickel-iron high-permeability laminations, with a radial gap so that the main reluctance controlling the flux in the magnetic circuit is that of the gap. The recording medium is arranged to move at steady speed, generally in a direction parallel to the leakage flux from the gap. Thus the wire or tape becomes magnetized longitudinally, and as it moves elemental magnets with like poles in juxtaposition are formed, their axial length being dependent on the frequency of the recorded signal and the speed of motion. The effective magnetization retained by the elemental magnets will be reduced by their self-demagnetization, which becomes

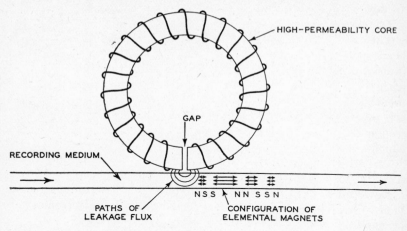

Fig. 7–1.—DIAGRAM OF MAGNETIC RECORDING AND/OR REPRODUCING MECHANISM.

greater as the effective axial length is reduced. Thus a reduction of response will be produced by a rise in the frequency, and the main problem is to obtain a good high-frequency response without excessive tape speeds. The demagnetization factor is also affected by fundamental magnetic properties and it can be shown to be roughly proportional to the ratio of remanence to coercive force. The most satisfactory results with materials for which this ratio is low have been achieved with those of lesser remanence. Although sensitivity is proportional to remanence, low sensitivity can be compensated by increased amplification.

Other causes of distortion lie in the non-linearity of the magnetization characteristics inherent in most materials. No possibility of controlling the shape of the magnetization curve is likely, but the introduction of an alternating bias at supersonic frequency helps materially in reducing non-linear effects ; this is now general practice.

A number of subsidiary considerations also enter into the choice of materials. The effect of an additional air-gap, actual or effective, between the recording medium and magnetic head has further important influence on the response to the higher frequencies, and for this reason it is essential to reduce the gap by running the recording wire or tape almost, if not quite, in contact with the pole pieces. The material must thus have a smooth surface, reasonable resistance to wear, and adequate strength to withstand tension in the winding mechanism.

The question of optimum wire—or tape—thickness [29] has also been considered. Thick tapes might be thought to give an inferior frequency response, as demagnetization effects increase with the cross-sectional area of the elemental magnets. Experiment, however, has shown that effects due to increase in thickness are masked by lack of penetration and that improvement in response by decreasing the thickness occurs only with dimensions which are mechanically impracticable.

The Magnetic Materials

Developments in materials have proceeded along two general lines. The original carbon-steel wire of Poulsen gave way to tungsten and other alloy steels following the general trend of permanent-magnet material developments. However, the later alloys such as Alnico, Alcomax, etc., cannot be produced in wire or tape form. Some attention has been given to ductile magnetic alloys, and the limited production of the copper-nickel-iron (" Cunife ") and copper-nickel-cobalt (" Cunico ") in Germany and the U.S.A. has resulted. The former has been used successfully in tape form for magnetic recording although expense and production difficulties have limited its application. Another successful development has been a non-magnetic base wire or tape which is covered with a magnetic coating by electrodeposition. In general, the properties of electrodeposited magnetic materials are favourable, as the characteristic high stress usually leads to a large coercive force. An example of such a material is a recording medium made by the Brush Development Company consisting of a brass wire coated with a nickel-cobalt alloy by electrodeposition. Of particular technical interest and of considerable promise are the austenitic nickel-chromium stainless steels.[30] Normally such alloys are non-magnetic, but on cold-working, magnetic properties appear on account of the formation of small particles of ferrite (magnetic) dispersed throughout the austenitic matrix. The properties developed are particularly suitable for magnetic recording, and can be adjusted and controlled by heat treatment of the wire.

The second class of recording media consists of non-metallic (e.g. paper or plastic) tapes, either coated or impregnated with powdered magnetic materials. In such tapes the subdivision of the magnetic constituent by inter-particle air-gaps effectively reduces the remanence and thus improves the ratio coercive force/ remanence. Limited use has been made of powdered Alnico dispersed in a plastic medium, but the materials so far most successfully developed and applied are the magnetic oxides of iron. These can be produced in the form of very fine particles ; these are desirable for the reduction of background noise, which might be caused by magnetic discontinuities in the recording medium comparable in size with the elemental magnets produced by the recorded impulses.

The above considerations have weight according to the severity of the requirements : e.g. the object may be the faithful reproduction of music, or only the intelligible reproduction of speech. Further applications of magnetic recording are found, in which the required magnetic properties are much less severe. An example is in the storage of signals in electronic computors, which has been successfully achieved by the use of an electroplated nickel film on a metal drum. As a further instance, the principle has been

TABLE 1. MAGNETIC RECORDING MATERIALS

Material	Remanence B_r	Coercive force H_c	K *	Form	Notes
	Wb/m²	A/m			
Carbon steel	0·9	4,000	1·0	Wire or tape.	Early uses now obsolete.
5% tungsten steel	1·0	5,200	1·2	Wire or tape.	Used in Marconi-Stille recording equipment by B.B.C. until recently.
Cunife (copper nickel-iron alloy)	0·6	40,000	15·0	Tape.	Limited use for recording in Germany and U.S.A. Costly and difficult to produce.
Nickel-cobalt	1·0	16,000	3·5	Plated on to brass wire or tape.	Limited use in U.S.A.
Stainless steel (18% Cr, 8% Ni).	0·06–0·3	16,000–32,000	30–60	Wire, cold drawn and heat treated.	Usually the normal stainless steel as supplied by various manufacturers. Special grade designated Tophet M produced by Wilbur B. Driver Co., U.S.A.
Magnetic oxide impregnated plastic.	0·03–0·08	8,000–32,000	60–90	Tape.	Magnetic oxide (Fe₂O₃ or Fe₃O₄) dispersed in cellulose acetate or p.v.c. tape. Produced in this country by E.M.I., G.E.C. and other manufacturers and in U.S.A. and Germany.

* Relative high-frequency response determined by ratio of coercive force to remanence.

used for the indication of the contents of tins in food-canning factories, where other means of labelling during processing are difficult, the magnetic properties of ordinary tinplate being adequate for a number of code patterns to be impressed and retained on the cans and subsequently revealed by an electronic scanner.[32]

Table 1 gives a list of materials which have found commercial application, with notes on properties, etc.

References

28. POULSEN, V. British Patent No. 8961 (1899).
29. KORNEI, O. " Frequency Response of Magnetic Recording," *Electronics*, 1947, **20**, August, pp. 124–28.
30. HOBSON, P. T. " Developments in Magnetic Recording," *Electronic Eng.*, Dec. 1947, **19**, 377–82.
    HOBSON, P. T., CHATT, E. S., and OSMOND, W. P. " Magnetic Study of Stainless Steel Wires," *Jnl. Iron & Steel Inst.*, 1948, **159**, 145–57.
31. PULLING, M. J. L. " The Magnetophon Sound Recording and Reproducing System," *B.I.O.S.* Final Report No. 951, H.M.S.O.
    THIESSEN, G. J. " The Magnetophon of A.E.G.," *B.I.O.S.* Final Report No. 207, H.M.S.O.
32. GUMPERTZ, D. G. " Magnetic Sorting on Unlabelled Food Cans," *Electronics*, Sept. 1952, 100–105.

8. MAGNETOSTRICTIVE MATERIALS

By

C. GORDON SMITH, M.A., A.M.I.E.E.

THE significance of magnetostriction in modern magnetic theory and its connection with fundamental properties has already been considered in Section 1.

Principles of Application

There are certain applications in which the magnetostrictive effect is of direct importance. These normally concern the construction of electro-mechanical transducers for which the utilization respectively of the Joule * and Villari † effects proves to be convenient, particularly when oscillations in the higher audio and ultrasonic ranges are required[1]. Although magnetostrictive effects are small (the change in length of a specimen of nickel, in which the Joule effect is relatively large, is only of the order of 30 parts in 10^6 when magnetized to saturation), large amplitudes may be built up by resonance in a suitably dimensioned magnetostrictive core excited by an alternating field of appropriate frequency, thus providing a powerful source of ultrasonic energy.

In most magnetostrictive applications other magnetic properties play an important part. For example, the efficiency of energy conversion may be reduced by excessive eddy-current and hysteresis losses. The value of incremental permeability may be important in the case of a transducer for converting mechanical vibrations. Another important requirement is some form of constant magnetic polarization of the vibrating specimen. The reasons for this will be apparent when studying Fig. 8–1, which shows a typical ‡ curve relating change in length to applied magnetic field. First, it should be noted that at low field strengths the slope of this curve decreases considerably. Thus, to maintain

---

* Change in dimensions due to magnetization.
† Change in magnetization due to stress.
‡ Data from different sources show considerable variation ; the curve given represents a fair average.

efficiency, bias is important in a transducer dealing with small energy levels such as in the reception of ultrasonic signals ; the optimum biasing point will be in the region of field strength equal to half or rather more of the saturation value. Further, unless a biasing field is applied the frequency of mechanical oscillation will be double that of the applied magnetic field, which is generally unfavourable and may produce an undesirable waveform.

In many types of apparatus a biasing field may be introduced without difficulty, but sometimes there will be technical difficulties in the design of the core or practical difficulties in the provision of the necessary permanent- or electro-magnet. In such a case the permanent magnetization of the magnetostrictive element itself may be employed ; success, however, depends on the use of a material with adequate magnetic remanence and coercive force, properties not usually found in conjunction with an optimum magnetostrictive effect.

Practical Materials

The commonest material is nickel, which has a large magneto-strictive effect. In general, for optimum properties, the metal should be of good commercial purity and fully annealed, but if

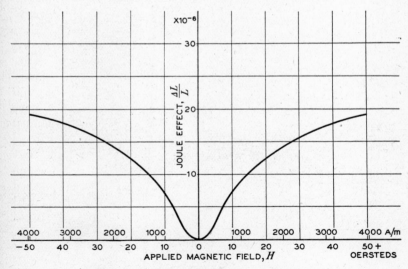

Fig. 8–1.—MAGNETOSTRICTIVE EFFECT IN NICKEL.

adequate remanence for self-polarization is required, the material may be used in a half-hard condition.   As alternatives, alloys in the nickel-iron series are promising ; as will be seen from Fig. 8–2, the magnetostrictive effects in the region of 20 and 45 per cent. nickel, although of opposite sign to that of nickel, are nearly as large.   The 45 per cent. nickel-iron alloy would have the further advantage of lower eddy-current losses on account of its higher resistivity (about eight times that of nickel), lower hysteresis losses and higher permeability.   Although eddy-current losses can be reduced by lamination, the optimum thickness would be in the region of 0·005 in. for nickel at 10 kc/s, a value which involves considerable expense in fabrication.   Thus an alloy with lower inherent losses presents practical advantages.   Where large power outputs are required, the dissipation of the energy consumed in losses may present problems, in the solution of which the nickel-iron alloys would present distinct advantages.

The cobalt-iron alloys are also of interest in view of the high magnetostrictive effects available with certain compositions (see Fig. 8–3).   Their use, however, has been commercially restricted

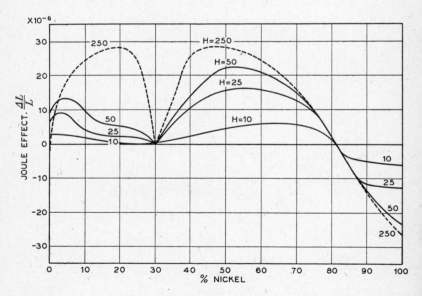

Fig. 8–2.—MAGNETOSTRICTIVE EFFECT OF NICKEL-IRON ALLOYS.   THE VALUES OF H ARE GIVEN IN OERSTEDS.

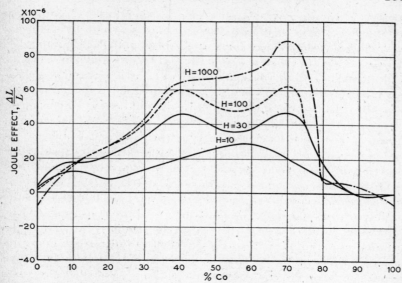

Fig. 8-3.—MAGNETOSTRICTIVE EFFECT OF COBALT-IRON ALLOYS. THE VALUES
OF H ARE GIVEN IN OERSTEDS.

on the grounds of cost and difficulty of fabrication, although
considerable progress has recently been made in overcoming the
latter. Limited use has also been made, more particularly in
Japan and Germany, of aluminium-iron alloys, investigated
originally by Masumuto [2] and developed under the name
"Alfer." These alloys are of lower technical efficiency, their
development having been due to nickel shortage.

Applications

Probably the most widespread application of ultrasonic vibrations is in their use for the detection and location of underwater
objects.[3] The original crude methods of echo ranging have been
extensively developed and improved, advantage being taken of
the possibilities in reflection and concentration of the shorter
ultrasonic waves. Magnetostrictive transducers using nickel rings
are employed both for the generation of pulses of energy (usually
with a frequency of 10 to 15 kc/s) and for the detection of
the reflections from a submerged object. The depth, determined by the time interval between transmitting and receiving

pulses, is usually recorded on a moving chart, and the direction of the object may be indicated with a focused beam by the usual scanning devices. The original application of depth sounding has been extended to the detection and location of various underwater objects such as submarines, fish shoals and wreckage, and magneto-strictive devices are now being installed in practically all sea-going vessels. Similar methods, but on a different scale and using in general much higher frequencies, may be used for the detection of internal flaws in the non-destructive testing of metal objects.

Other uses of ultrasonics which have aroused considerable interest of recent years depend on the peculiar physical effects of high-frequency vibrations on various materials. As examples, the emulsification of oils, dispersion of solids in liquids, and the killing of bacteria may be mentioned. An interesting use is the ultrasonic soldering iron developed by Mullard Ltd., for the tinning of aluminium, in which the effects of ultrasonic vibration are used to cause the continuous dispersal of the oxide film which tends to form on the aluminium surface. In such processes considerable energy is usually needed and magnetostrictive transducers are particularly suitable on account of their robustness and power-handling capabilities. In other applications for which high intensities are not called for, piezo-electric and ferro-electric transducers are frequently used. These have relatively poor mechanical strength. In general, apart from the question of power output, the inherent physical characteristics of magnetostrictive transducers tend to be more suitable for the lower frequencies, whilst those of piezo- and ferro-electric devices favour use at the higher frequencies.

Magnetostrictive materials have been used in vibrating frequency standards, in which the frequency of a valve-maintained oscillator is controlled by the mechanical vibration of a suitable magnetostrictive element. Alloys with special properties are called for when a high precision of frequency is needed. It is fortunate that alloys already developed on account of their constancy of elastic modulus (and thus vibrational frequency) at different temperatures show in most cases appreciable magnetostrictive effects. These are modifications of the well-known Invar type, e.g. Elinvar, Chronovar, Ni-Span " C," etc. The behaviour of alloys of this type with and without minor modifications has been studied in detail by Ide [4] for frequency-standard applications.

References

1. BERGMANN, L. " Der Ultraschall," Pub. S. Hirzel Verlag, Zurich, 1949, 5th edition. (Translation of early edition, Bell & Sons, London, 1938.)
2. MASUMOTO, H. " Dynamical Characteristics of Magnetostriction Alloy ' Alfer.' " *Sci. Rep. Res. Inst.*, Tohoku Univ. Series A, June 1950, 2, 413–19.
3. GALWAY, H. " Echo Sounding at Sea (British Practice)," Pitman, London, 1951.
4. IDE, J. M. " Magnetostrictive Alloys with Low Temperature Coefficients of Frequency," *Proc. I.R.E.*, 1934, 22, 177–90.

APPENDIX

INTRODUCTION TO M.K.S. MAGNETIC UNITS

By

PROFESSOR M. G. SAY, Ph.D., M.Sc., M.I.E.E.

THE unit system employed in this book is the metre-kilogramme-second system in its rationalized form. The M.K.S. system was developed in 1901 by the Italian engineer Giorgi, and independently three years later by Professor Robertson of Bristol. It was later brought to the attention of the International Electrotechnical Commission, which in 1935 signified approval of the system for international use. Certain details were not finally settled until the 1938 and 1939 meetings, and the I.E.C. formally adopted the rationalized M.K.S. system in 1950. However, well before that date the system had become common in Europe and almost universal in the United States.

Basic M.K.S. Units

The M.K.S. units form an absolute system in which the electrical units are the commonly used " practical " volt, ampere, ohm, coulomb, farad, henry, joule and watt. The unit of power on a basis of mechanics must also be the watt. This follows automatically with the kilogramme, metre and second as units of mass, length and time respectively, because the unit of force is that necessary to endow a mass of one kilogramme with an acceleration of one metre per second per second. This unit of force is called the newton. A power of one newton-metre per second is one watt, and an energy of one newton-metre is one joule.

The magnetic units are selected to correspond with these electrical and mechanical units to give a one-to-one ratio between related quantities. For this purpose the magnetic and electric properties of free space are essentially recognized, and are not suppressed or ignored as has not been uncommon in the use of the classic C.G.S. electromagnetic and electrostatic unit systems.

The C.G.S. Unit Systems

In the C.G.S. electromagnetic (e.m.) system, the unit pole (and thence unit current, charge, etc.) is defined from

$$f = m_1 m_2 / \mu_0 s^2$$

taking $f = 1$ dyne, the distance $s = 1$ cm, and μ_0 as unity. In the C.G.S. electrostatic (e.s.) system the unit charge (and thence unit current, etc.) is defined from

$$f = q_1 q_2 / \varkappa_0 s^2$$

with $f = 1$ dyne and $s = 1$ cm., and taking $\varkappa_0$ as unity. But, by Maxwell's electromagnetic theory, in any consistent system the product $\mu_0 \varkappa_0 = 1/c^2$, where c is the velocity of free-space electromagnetic propagation in the chosen units of length and time. It follows therefore that the C.G.S. e.m. and e.s. systems are not mutually consistent : a unit quantity in one system differs in magnitude from the unit of the same physical quantity in the other. Thus 1 e.m.u. of current has the magnitude of 3×10^{10} e.s.u. of current, and neither has the magnitude of 1 A.

For many years engineers and (to a limited extent) physicists have been using a mixture of C.G.S. e.m. and e.s. units, together with the " practical " system (volt, ampere, ohm, henry, farad) based on decimal multiples of the e.m. units. In general, the " practical " units have been employed only in circuitry, the basic e.m. units only for magnetic-field problems, and the e.s. units only for electrostatics. Inconvenient conversions involving powers of 10 and of c have had to be employed to relate field quantities to circuit theory.

The M.K.S. system replaces these three mutually conflicting systems by one comprehensive, unified system. It involves certain small sacrifices that are greatly outweighed by important and valuable advantages. The question of rationalization is a separate one, but the reform is most conveniently made simultaneously with the adoption of M.K.S. units. The M.K.S. system in its rationalized form has been commended by the Institution of Electrical Engineers ; while B.S. 1637 : 1950 defines the system and gives a historical note on its development.

The M.K.S. Unit System

This is an absolute system with the metre [m], kilogramme [kg] and second [s] respectively as units of length, mass and time.

The two former are defined arbitrarily by international platinum standards maintained at Sèvres, and the latter is 1/86400 of a mean solar day. The *electrical* units are the familiar practical ones—volt [V], ampere [A], ohm [Ω], coulomb [C], farad [F], henry [H], joule [J] and watt [W]. The *mechanical* units are, for force the newton [N], for energy the joule and for power the watt : these link conveniently with the established electrical units in the manner already described.

The absolute volt and ampere are fixed (*a*) by the convention that $1 V \times 1 A = 1 W$, and (*b*) by the definition of the ampere as that steady current which, maintained in two parallel conductors of infinite length and negligible cross-section, and separated by a distance of 1 m. *in vacuo*, produces between the conductors a mechanical force of 2×10^{-7} N per m length. The force is conceived to arise magnetically in accordance with the " interaction law " based on experiment : the current in one wire is taken as lying in a magnetic field produced by the other. For a length l metres of a parallel-wire system with spacing s metres, a current I_1 in one wire produces at the other wire a magnetic flux density proportional to I_1, inversely proportional to the distance s, and dependent on the magnetic property μ_0 of the surrounding free space. The second current lies in this magnetic flux density and the resulting mutual force is

$$f = KI_1I_2\mu_0l/s \text{ newtons}$$

where K is a constant. In the terms of the definition of the ampere, $I_1 = I_2 = 1$ A, $l = s = 1$ m ; and in consequence

$$K\mu_0 = 2 \times 10^{-7}.$$

The value of K, and consequently that of μ_0, depends on the manner in which current is related to magnetomotive force, F. The relation * may be taken as $F = 4\pi I$ or as $F = I$: the former gives the *unrationalized* and the latter the *rationalized* system.

The concept of the isolated magnetic pole is now commonly discarded, and magnetomotive force is treated as a line-integral of magnetic field strength. Therefore, taking $F = I$, the m.m.f. per metre length of a circular path of radius s is $H = I/2\pi s$, the

* I represents the current-turn product, which is dimensionally the same as current, [A].

flux density produced by it is $B = \mu_0 H = \mu_0 I/2\pi s$, and the force equation above becomes

$$f = (1/2\pi)I_1 I_2 \mu_0 l/s,$$

which gives $K = 1/2\pi$. In consequence, $\mu_0 = 4\pi/10^7$. (As a further consequence of the $\mu_0 \varkappa_0$ product, $\varkappa_0 = 1/36\pi \times 10^9$).

If the m.m.f. is taken as $4\pi I$, then $\mu_0 = 10^{-7}$ (and $\varkappa_0$ is then $1/9 \times 10^9$). This alternative will not be considered further, here, since this book uses rationalized M.K.S. units.

Rationalized M.K.S. Magnetic Units

Consider a single-turn resistanceless coil *in vacuo*. To establish a current of 1 A in it requires the application of a voltage for a time such that the time-integral of the voltage is proportional to the final current and independent of the manner in which the current changes from zero to 1 A. According to the usual concept, the space in and around the coil becomes the seat of a magnetic flux Φ which is measured by the voltage-time integral :

$$\Phi = \int v \, dt \text{ [volt} \times \text{second (V.s)]}.$$

The more usual name for the flux unit is the weber [Wb], which has the physical dimensions of [V.s]. The flux is also proportional to the current, i.e.,

$$\Phi = LI,$$

where L is the self-inductance in henrys [H] corresponding to [Wb/A] or [V.s/A]. The recoverable energy stored in the magnetic field is

$$W = \tfrac{1}{2}\Phi I \text{ [Wb} \times \text{A} = \text{V.s} \times \text{A} = \text{J]}.$$

Experiment shows that if the coil is arranged so that the magnetic field is uniform within it and negligible outside (e.g. by completing the magnetic circuit through other coils), the magneto-motive force of the coil current accounts completely for the flux within its length. Then the total flux for a given coil current is proportional to the cross-sectional area A and inversely proportional to the length l. The flux density is $B = \Phi/A$ [Wb/m²] and the magnetizing force (or m.m.f. per metre) is $H = I/l$ [A/m]. Then the density is proportional to the magnetizing force and can be written

$$B = \mu_0 H. \quad \text{[Wb/m}^2\text{]}.$$

If A is 1 m^2 and l is 1 m, the inductance of the unit coil is

$$L = \frac{\Phi}{I} = \frac{B}{H} = \mu_0 \quad \left[\frac{\text{V.s}}{\text{m}^2} \cdot \frac{\text{m}}{\text{A}} = \frac{\text{V.s}}{\text{A.m}} = \frac{\text{H}}{\text{m}} \right].$$

The cubic unit coil has thus an inductance $\mu_0 = 4\pi/10^7$ [H/m]. The term " absolute permeability of free space," or better the " magnetic space constant," is used to describe μ_0.

Corresponding to the total energy $\frac{1}{2}\Phi I$ [J] there is the energy density

$$\frac{1}{2}BH = \frac{1}{2}B^2/\mu_0 \text{ [J/m}^3\text{]}.$$

If the vacuum in which the coil is immersed is filled with magnetic matter of relative permeability μ_r, the self-inductance is found to increase μ_r times for the same magnetizing force, so that now

$$B = \mu_r\mu_0H = \mu H \text{ [Wb/m}^2\text{]}.$$

The additional density may be considered to be due to the intensity of magnetization J of the material in [Wb/m^2] :

$$B = B_0 + J = \mu_0H + J \text{ [Wb/m}^2\text{]}.$$

Analogously, the relative permeability may be expressed as the sum of the free-space relative permeability (unity) and the susceptibility of the material :

$$\mu_r = 1 + \chi.$$

TABLE 1.   BASIC PHYSICAL QUANTITIES

Physical quantity	Equation	M.K.S. unit *	C.G.S. unit	Conversion	
Length .	l	m	cm	1 m	$= 10^2$ cm
Area . .	$A = l^2$	m^2	cm^2	1 m^2	$= 10^4$ cm^2
Volume .	$U = l^3$	m^3	cm^3	1 m^3	$= 10^6$ cm^3
Mass . .	m	kg	g	1 kg	$= 10^3$ g
Time . .	t	s	s		
Velocity .	$u = l/t$	m/s	cm/s	1 m/s	$= 10^2$ cm/s
Acceleration	$a = l/t^2$	m/s^2	cm/s^2	1 m/s^2	$= 10^2$ cm/s^2
Force .	$f = ma$	N	dyne	1 N	$= 10^5$ dynes
Torque .	$T = fl$	N-m	dyne-cm	1 N-m	$= 10^7$ dyne-cm
Energy .	W	J	erg	1 J	$= 10^7$ ergs
Power .	$P = W/t$	W	erg/s	1 W	$= 10^7$ ergs/s

* The abbreviations used for unit-names are explained on pages 191-192.

TABLE 2.   MAGNETIC QUANTITIES

Magnetic quantity	Rationalized M.K.S. system		C.G.S. e.m.—practical system *		Conversion
	Expression	Unit †	Expression	Unit	
Magnetomotive force	$F = IN$	[AT]	$F = (4\pi/10)IN$	[Gilbert]	1 AT $= 4\pi \cdot 10^{-1}$ gilbert.
Magnetizing force	$H = F/l$	[AT/m]	$H = F/l$	[Oersted]	1 AT/m $= 4\pi \cdot 10^{-3}$ oersted.
Magnetic space-constant	$\mu_0 = 4\pi \cdot 10^{-7}$	[H/m]	$\mu_0 = 1$		
Flux density	$B = \mu_r\mu_0 H$	[Wb/m²]	$B = \mu_r H$	[Gauss]	1 Wb/m² $= 10^4$ gauss.
Flux	$\Phi = BA$	[Wb]	$\Phi = BA$	[Maxwell]	1 Wb $= 10^8$ maxwells.
Intensity of magnetization	$J = B - \mu_0 H$	[Wb/m²]	$J = (B-H)/4\pi$	[Gauss/4π]	
Reluctance	$S = F/\Phi$	[AT/Wb]	$S = F/\Phi$	[Gilbert/maxwell]	1 AT/Wb $= 4\pi \cdot 10^{-9}$ c.g.s.
Field energy density	$w = \tfrac{1}{2}BH$	[J/m³]	$w = \tfrac{1}{2}BH/4\pi$	[Erg/cm³]	1 J/m³ $= 10$ ergs/cm³
			$w = \tfrac{1}{2}BH$	[Gauss-oersted]	1 J/m³ $= 4\pi \cdot 10$ gauss-oersted.

* Magnetic-field quantities in C.G.S. e.m. units ; current in amperes.
† The abbreviations used for unit names are explained on pages 191–192.

It will be noted that the use of the weber gives Faraday's law in the form

$$e = - d\Phi/dt \text{ [V]}$$

without the factor of 10^{-8} required for this law in the older mixture of C.G.S. e.m. unit and practical unit (maxwell and volt). Rationalization leads to simplification in the m.m.f. relations, whereby the m.m.f. $F = I$ instead of $0\cdot4\pi I$, and $H = I/l$ instead of $0\cdot4\pi I/l$: it further simplifies the energy density to $\frac{1}{2}BH$ [J/m³] in place of $BH/8\pi$ [ergs/cm.³]. The unit relations are summarized in Tables 1 and 2.

The unfamiliarity of rationalized M.K.S. magnetic units is their only disadvantage. The maxwell, gauss and oersted must be replaced by the weber, weber per square metre and ampere (-turn) per metre. With the flux and flux density the changes are merely in the position of a decimal point, as the weber is 10^8 maxwells and the weber per square metre is 10^4 gauss. The latter is actually more convenient, as the flux densities set up in air-gaps for engineering purposes will frequently be found to have values of the order of unity. In the case of magnetizing force, the awkward factor 4π occurs in converting H values from oersteds to ampere (-turns) per metre. However, users of B/H magnetic data frequently use a " rationalized " version with B in gauss and H in ampere-turns per centimetre : in this case the conversion is again a simple decimal matter, as 1 A/m is 10^{-2} A/cm.

Rationalization also affects the absolute permeability $\mu = B/H$ of a magnetic material. But if the magnetic properties of free space are clearly recognized as in the expression $\mu = \mu_r\mu_0$, the relative permeability μ_r remains unchanged in its familiar form and value.

INDEX